The Big Book of Small Presses & Independent Publishers

Other Books by
Marylee MacDonald

FICTION

Body Language
Bonds of Love and Blood
Montpelier Tomorrow
The Rug Bazaar

NONFICTION

The Quiet Indoor Revolution
Repairing Historic Flat Plaster, Walls, and Ceilings

The Big Book of Small Presses & Independent Publishers

Small presses, book contests,
university presses, and independent publishers
for "unagented" authors

Marylee MacDonald

TEMPE, AZ

Publisher's Cataloging-in-Publication Data
Names: MacDonald, Marylee, author.
Title: The big book of small presses & independent publishers : small presses, book contests, university presses, and independent publishers for "unagented" authors / Marylee MacDonald.

Description: First edition. | Tempe, AZ : Grand Canyon Press, [2020]

Identifiers: ISBN: 978-1-951479-19-0 (paperback) | 978-1-951479-20-6 (Amazon paperback) | 978-1-951479-04-6 (Kindle) | 978-1-951479-05-3 (epub) | 978-1-951479-06-0 (PDF) | 978-1-951479-08-4 (ePib) | 978-1-951479-07-7 (ibook)

Subjects: LCSH: Publishers and publishing--United States--Directories. | Small presses--United States-- Directories. | Book contests--United States--Directories. | University presses--United States-- Directories. | Private presses--United States--Directories. | Authors, American-- Handbooks, manuals, etc. | LCGFT: Directories. | BISAC: LANGUAGE ARTS & DISCIPLINES / Publishers & Publishing Industry. | LANGUAGE ARTS & DISCIPLINES / Writing / Business Aspects.

Classification: LCC: PN161 .M33 2020 | DDC: 070.5/90973--dc23
386 pages; cm

Publisher's Note: This is a work of nonfiction. Representations of businesses, companies, events, institutions, and requirements for publication are gathered from the publishers' websites. Obtaining specific information about a publishers' ability to fulfill its contractual obligations is the responsibility of the author. The listings in this book are for informational purposes only.

Ordering Information:
Quantity sales. Special discounts are available on quantity purchases by corporations, associations, and others. For details, contact the "Special Sales Department" at the address below.

Grand Canyon Press
P.O. Box 27733
Tempe, AZ 85285

For writers everywhere.

May your dreams come true.

Table of Contents

"A Book is only the Heart's Portrait—every Page a Pulse."

—*Emily Dickinson*

Preface

Have you been frustrated in your attempts to find an agent? Or if you have one, has your agent been unable to sell your book? Have you waited months or years to learn whether publishers are going to bite?

I have and that's why I wrote this book. This book contains all the independent publishers listed on the Duotrope, NewPages, and Poets & Writers websites. These three sites list independent presses, book contests, small publishers, and university presses. I've scoured their lists to find non-fee-charging publishers who read "unagented" manuscripts. These presses allow authors to directly submit, without the intervention of an agent.

Many independent presses publish with POD (print on demand) technology, the same technology used by Amazon's Kindle Direct Publishing and Ingram Spark. If you want to self-publish, then that's certainly an option. Both Ingram and Amazon provide excellent tools to help you upload your manuscript and produce an e-book or print book. Additionally, Ingram lists your book in its catalog, making it possible for bookstores to order it. However, even if you succeed in self-publishing a print copy of your book through Ingram, it's hard to get a bookstore to stock any POD-produced book.

Customers who want to read your book can ask a bookstore to order it from Ingram, but few bookstores have the shelf space to stock anything other than the books that are appearing on the *USA Today* and *New York Times'* bestseller lists. Bookstores will absolutely *not* stock a book produced by Amazon. That's because brick-and-mortar stores are in a fight-to-the-death with Amazon.

If you want to see your book in a bookstore, you would be wise to look for a regional or university press that uses a book distributor. These include Small Press Distribution and Publishers Group West. If a publisher has a book distributor, the publisher will normally say so on their website. If they don't and bookstore distribution is important to you, then inquire.

Small and independent presses come in all shapes and sizes. Some presses are the result a single person's dedication to publishing. If that's the case, burnout is a high probability and the press might cease taking submissions until the editor gets "caught up." Other independent presses have a team of three to five people reading manuscripts and editing, designing, and producing books. Still others run contests that have an entry fee and a cash prize. Still others are affiliated with bookstores or literary communities.

And, of course, some are affiliated with universities.

In some cases a department is charged with training students to work in the publishing industry. The department sponsors a book contest, and the students, with faculty supervision, select, edit, format, and market the winning book. Other university-affiliated book contests are housed in Creative Writing departments, and students are the first readers. Such contests often have hundreds of entries, and only a single winner. The winning manuscript will then be handed off to the university press, and its editors will assume responsibility for book production.

University presses occasionally sponsor prestigious annual fiction awards, such as the Iowa Short Fiction Award or the Flannery O'Connor Award for Short Fiction. These are extremely competitive. Unfortunately, very few university presses publish fiction; however, you might find a university press that will take a biography or memoir or regional guidebook.

The profit margin in book publishing is extremely small. Most of the publishers in this book pay little or nothing in the way of an advance. But, then again, they're not asking you to shell out thousands of dollars, which is what happens if you decide to publish with a "vanity press". According to Wikipedia, vanity presses include the American Biographical Institute; Dorrance Publishing; Famous Poets Society; Poetry.com, The International Library of Poetry; Tate Publishing & Enterprises; Vantage Press; and Xlibris. The publishers in this book definitely do not qualify as vanity presses. With a couple of exceptions—such as contest entry fees or the nominal charge to upload a manuscript through Submittable—most charge nothing.

Along with each listing and my attempt to condense information that seems most relevent to you, I've included categories for the kinds of books each publisher is interested in publishing. These include memoir, nonfiction, romance, thriller, horror, poetry, and literary fiction. I've also listed those that say they welcome new writers. I hope this will allow you to go through the listings quickly and find publishers that might be a potential match for what you've written. Take the time to get a sense for the publisher's "wish list" and formatting requirements, and then go for it.

Good luck! I know that on this list, there's a publisher for each and every one of you.

Marylee MacDonald
Santa Rosa, CA

Publishers

18thWall Productions

submissions@18thwall.com

Fairy Tales, Novel, Horror, Fantasy, Mystery

18thWall Productions is always open to novel submissions. Send them your first 20,000 words, a full outline, and a cover letter (e.g. in your e-mail) where you tell them something about yourself (including previous credits) and what led you to write your novel. Don't stress it. A mangled cover letter won't kill your chances. Like with any first date, the best advice is this: just be yourself.

They prefer that your novel submission follow the William Shunn format outline, except that you use Times New Roman. It's easier on their poor editorial eyes. (If you are not familiar with standard formatting requirements, you should definitely go to the website below and take a look. Most publishers expect manuscripts to be formatted according to Shunn's guidelines.)

www.shunn.net/format/novel.html

Your e-mail header should be Novel Submission: Title, Author's Name, Wordcount. E-mail your submission packet to the address above.

Do not submit a manuscript with hyperlinks. If a link is required, they will discuss that upon acceptance.

They are not open to simultaneous submissions.

4RV Publishing

2912 Rankin Terrace
Edmond, OK 73013
President@4rvpublishingllc.com
www.4rvpublishing.com/manuscript-submissions.php

YA Fiction, New Adult

Check their website for specific submission dates. Submissions for manuscripts for Children's Books are closed until further notice. However, they are open for Tweens & Teens, Young Adult, New Adult, Fiction, and Nonfiction. Biblically-based submissions are wanted especially for New Adult, Fiction, and Nonfiction.

New Adult fiction bridges the gap between Young Adult and Adult genres. It typically features protagonists between the ages of 18 and 30. The genre tends to focus on issues prevalent in the young adult world, such as leaving home for university and getting a job. New adult is typically considered a subcategory of adult literature rather than young adult literature.

7.13Books

www.713books.com/submit/

Literary Fiction, Story Collection, Novel, New Writers

Submissions are restricted to writers who have not yet published a book of literary fiction. 7.13 is a small press that will put out beautiful books and give a new author a chance to experience most, if not all, of what it's like to have a successful debut novel in the world.

They are taking submissions for publication in 2021 and will require that the manuscript be between 45,000 and 100,000 words.

As traditional literary publishing shrinks and becomes increasingly elitist, 7.13 Books is part of a vibrant small press ecosystem that is passionate about keeping literature alive and saving quality manuscripts that have fallen through the widening cracks of a backsliding, inefficient industry. As a publisher, 7.13 Books aspires to be a partner in getting writers started on their careers as professional authors.

Leland Cheuk, founder of the press, is the author of the story collection *Letters From Dinosaurs* (Thought Catalog Books, 2016) and the novel *The Misadventures of Pong* (CCLaP, 2015). A MacDowell Colony Fellow, Cheuk's work has appeared *in Salon, Electric Literature, The Rumpus, Kenyon Review, Prairie Schooner, [PANK] Magazine,* and elsewhere.

Abuzz Press
www.abuzzpress.com/

Novel, Romance

Abuzz Press is part of the BookLocker.com, Inc. family of businesses, which includes BookLocker.com, one of the first POD and e-book publishers (established in 1998), and WritersWeekly.com, one of the oldest and most respected sites on freelance writing. They take the initial financial risk, and you agree to take the reins on book promotion.

In other words, Abuzz Press pays the design and publication fees, which include: interior formatting assistance, professional cover design (no boring templates), ISBN and barcode, printer setup, and print proof (the first printed/bound copy of your book, which will ship directly to you for approval). Their services include e-book formatting and conversion. Once the book is on the market, they will provide you with their free marketing guide, and then you start promoting the book. Since Abuzz Press is taking the financial risk, you agree to give Abuzz exclusive publishing rights for a period of three years.

If you prefer to pay the fees up front, and not assign exclusive rights, contact their publishing services division, BookLocker.com.

www.publishing.booklocker.com/

Academy Chicago Publishers

Cynthia Sherry

csherry@chicagoreviewpress.com

www.chicagoreviewpress.com/information-for-authors--amp--agents-pages-100.php

Memoirs, Nonfiction, Young Adult

Chicago Review Press works collaboratively with their authors, and they pride themselves on developing longstanding author-publisher relationships. They value communication, and at every stage of the publishing process they solicit authors' ideas and feedback. Not only do they work hard to create bestselling books, but they also endeavor to make the publishing experience an enjoyable one.

They are interested in publishing high-quality nonfiction that will sell year after year. They look for books with a well-defined, passionate target audience. Chicago Review Press publishes nonfiction in the following categories: African-American interest, autobiography/biography, DIY, film, food and drink (not cookbooks), history, music, parenting, politics, popular culture, popular science, social science, sports, regional (Midwest), nature/outdoor/travel, true crime, and women's interest. Chicago Review Press also publishes an award-winning line of children's and young adult titles.

E-mail a brief query to one of their acquiring editors:

- Jerome Pohlen at jpohlen@chicagoreviewpress.com for popular science, DIY, U.S. history, pop culture, and children's nonfiction activity books.
- Yuval Taylor at ytaylor@chicagoreviewpress.com for African-American interest, film, food and drink (not cookbooks), music, politics, sports, and true crime, as well as autobiography, biography, and history.

Acre Books

Nicola Mason, Editor
masonnf@acre-books.com
www.acre-books.com

Historical Fiction, Story Collection, YA Fiction, Sci fi, Poetry, Nonfiction

Acre Books, the book-publishing offshoot of *The Cincinnati Review*, aims to build on the excellence that its parent publication has become known for. Like *CR*, their small press will focus on surprising, imaginative, and absorbing works—of poetry, fiction, literary nonfiction, and hybrid forms—that are expertly crafted and beautifully polished, and that engage readers aesthetically as well as emotionally.

They are devoted to finding, and bringing to a broad readership, remarkably talented newcomers. Initially they will bring out 4 to 5 titles annually, but they intend in the coming years to expand their lists and their staff. Visit their webpage to subscribe to their mailing list.

There are two submission periods per year. Submission Guidelines can be found here:

www.acre-books.com/about-us/submissions/

Adelaide Books

Nicola Mason, Editor
info@adelaidebooks.org
istinadba@gmail.com
www.adelaidebooks.org/submissions.html

Historical Fiction, Story Collection, Memoirs, Spirituality, Creative Nonfiction, Nonfiction

Adelaide Books publishes novels (literary fiction, historical fiction, and romance), collections of short stories, poetry, memoirs, as well as creative nonfiction books on history, spirituality, religion, and esoteric teachings.

They accept only well-written, responsibly researched manuscripts. Your book must be both informative and engaging to the reader and written in lively, lucid prose. The topic must have broad, long-term appeal. The sources you rely on must be thoroughly documented and not infringe on any existing copyrights. Writers are responsible for supplying all photographs, maps, and other graphics their book may need. Poetry manuscripts must consist of at least 60 poems. Short story collections and novellas must have at least 20,000 words.

Ad Lumen Press

www.adlumenpress.submittable.com/submit

Story Collection, Memoirs, Novel, Literary Fiction

Ad Lumen Press is accepting manuscripts of full-length literary novels and memoirs from emerging authors who may or may not have previously published a book-length work. Submissions must include a cover letter and two- to three-page synopsis of the work. Manuscripts should be between 60,000 and 120,000 words. Submit between May 15 and August 15.

Although the press does publish collections of poetry and short stories, they do not accept unsolicited submissions in these genres. Likewise, they do not accept story proposals or genre fiction. Be patient with their selection process as it may take up to four months from the submission deadline to hear back from them.

Ad Lumen Press was founded at American River College in Sacramento, California in 2013 by author and professor Christian Kiefer. Building on the thirty-year publishing history of *American River Review*, the college's nationally recognized literary and art magazine, Ad Lumen Press is the nation's only university-style literary-press housed at a community college. While the press publishes poetry, novellas, short story collections, and literary nonfiction, only novels and book-length memoirs currently are accepted in their unsolicited submission process. Ad Lumen Press seeks to publish works of high artistic and/or literary merit from emerging voices across genres and from throughout the country, with a special emphasis on works from the greater Sacramento region.

Alaska Literary Series

UA-acquisitions@alaska.edu
www.alaska.edu/uapress/authors/

Creative Nonfiction, Poetry, Literary Fiction, Novel, Story Collection

Submissions are restricted to those with a connection to or writing about Alaska or the circumpolar north.

The Alaska Literary Series publishes poetry, fiction, and literary nonfiction. Successful manuscripts have a strong connection to Alaska or the circumpolar north, are written by people living in the far north, or both. They prefer writing that makes the northern experience available to the world, and they choose manuscripts that offer compelling literary insights into the human condition.

Alban Lake Publishing
www.albanlakepublishing.com/

Fantasy, Novella, New Writers, Novel, Sci fi, Horror, Paranormal, Steampunk

Alban Lake Publishing is a small, independent publishing enterprise with preferences for science fiction and fantasy novels, novellas, short stories, and poetry. They also consider spooky [not gory] horror, steampunk, paranormal, and vampire. They publish material suitable for experienced readers, and they publish material for younger readers They publish experienced writers and beginning writers, and all levels in between. They do work with beginning writers, and frequently comment on submitted manuscripts.

For more details on submissions, go here:
www.albanlakepublishing.com/other-submissions

Albert Whitman & Company

250 South Northwest Highway
Suite 320
Park Ridge, IL 60068
submissions@albertwhitman.com
www.albertwhitman.com

YA Fiction, Fiction, Children's Books, New Writers, Novel

Albert Whitman & Company currently has an open submissions policy. They will read and review unagented manuscripts and proposals for picture books, middle-grade fiction, and young adult novels. Read the following instructions carefully. They will not review any submissions that do not follow their guidelines.

Due to the great number of submissions they receive, they cannot respond to individual submissions unless they have further interest. Authors may assume that after six months they are not interested in publishing your work.

Authors may send their work to other publishers at the same time. AW&C does not require exclusive submissions.

FOR ALL SUBMISSIONS:
Include a cover letter in the body of the e-mail (please see individual category guidelines for cover letter tips).
Include contact information with phone number.

- Attach manuscripts as Microsoft Word DOCs (preferred) or PDFs. File sizes cannot be larger than 4MB.
- Subject line must be formatted according to individual category guidelines. E-mails that do not use the subject line formatting may not be read.

PICTURE BOOKS:
They are seeking: Fiction and nonfiction manuscripts for picture books for children ages 1 to 8. Word count: Up to 1000 words. A cover letter (in body of e-mail) should include the following:

- Brief description of story
- Short bio mentioning previous publications or other background

information relevant to the story
- Please provide titles for up to three comparable books published in the past five years. These should be books that have a similar audience to the book being submitted and that the author feels will compare with the submitted book in the marketplace. Explain how the submitted manuscript is different from these books.

It is not necessary to provide illustrations with the story text. If the story is illustrated, the publisher will review text and art separately. (Note that they may be interested in the story but not the artwork, or vice versa). Send illustrated work in PDF or JPEG attachments. File size not to exceed 4MB.

Send e-mail and attachments with a subject line that reads: "PICTURE BOOK: (story title) by (author name)."

MIDDLE GRADE FICTION:
They are seeking fiction queries and sample pages for middle-grade novels for children up to age 12 and with a word count of up to 35,000 words. For more information, go here:

www.albertwhitman.com/submission-guidelines-for-unrepresented-authors/

Algonquin Books of Chapel Hill

225 Varick Street
New York, NY 10014-4381
(919) 933-0272
dialogue@algonquin.com
www.workman.com/work-with-us/author-submissions#algonquin

Essays, Nonfiction, Creative Nonfiction

A highly competitive publisher, Algonquin is not open for fiction submissions at this time unless you have had the good fortune to be invited to submit by an editor. (The best way to meet an editor is at a writers' conference. Use Google to find where Algonquin editors have agreed to take pitches from conference attendees.)

If you have another kind of book, you might want to check out the submissions page for their parent company, Workman Press. When submitting a proposal, please keep in mind that it may take up to three months for editors to review it.

They also have other niche publishing entities variously called "The Experiment," the "Storey Project," and "Timber Press."

Algonquin has wide distribution and access to the bookstore market, so authors with books that might fit into any of their desired genres would be well advised to submit. The mailing addresses and contact information from these other publishing arms differ from that of the main office. Check the website for instructions on what and how to submit.

Alice James Books

238 Main Street
Farmington, ME 04938
www.alicejamesbooks.org/

New Writers, Poetry

Alice James publishes the best contemporary poetry by established and emerging voices. The press is committed to publishing books that matter by authors who may otherwise go unheard. They collaborate closely with authors in the publishing process.

Manuscripts for the 2020 Alice James Award are accepted via Submittable. Note that Alice James Books does not accept unsolicited manuscripts outside of the award period. The award period ends on November 1.

The Alice James Award welcomes submissions from emerging as well as established poets. Entrants must reside in the United States.

The winner receives $2000, book publication, and distribution through Consortium, a small press book distributor. In addition to the winning manuscript, one or more additional manuscripts may be chosen for publication as the Editor's Choice.

To submit electronically, visit their Submittable site. For details on submission guidelines and how to send a hardcopy submission, review the guidelines on their website:

www.alicejames.submittable.com/submit

All Things That Matter Press

allthingsthatmatterpress@gmail.com
www.allthingsthatmatterpress.com/submissionrequirements.htm

Sci fi, Story Collection, Memoirs, Novella, Novel, Nonfiction, New Writers

All Things That Matter Press seeks to publish those books that help the author share their "self" with the world. Every author believes they have something to say, and this is a press that is open to unique perspectives. While their focus is on spiritual, self-growth, personal transformation, and books with a strong message, they understand that self expression occurs in poetry, collections of short stories, science fiction, thrillers, and even novels with a bit of romance. If it is good, they will take a look. Authors should understand that this is a POD publisher. Their website has helpful resources on book marketing, but the publishers do not endeavor to market the authors' books.

Allen & Unwin

fridaypitch@allenandunwin.com
www.allenandunwin.com/submission-guidelines

Australian, New Writers, Nonfiction, Memoirs, Novel

This is a literary, mainstream press with no interest in romance, sci fi, or short story collections. An Australian publisher, they are currently looking for bios of Aussies. Allen & Unwin know how difficult it can be for writers to get their work in front of publishers, which is why they've created their innovative and pioneering submissions system

The Friday Pitch allows for writers of all genres to have their work considered by one of their in-house Submission Editors. Select the genre of your work, and follow the links to the appropriate submissions page for more details.

Adult Fiction, Nonfiction and Illustrated Submissions:
www.allenandunwin.com/about-allen-and-unwin/submission-guidelines/the-friday-pitch

Children's and Young Adult Submissions:
www.allenandunwin.com/about-allen-and-unwin/submission-guidelines/children-young-adult-submission-guidelines

Academic Submissions:
www.allenandunwin.com/about-allen-and-unwin/submission-guidelines/academic-submission-guidelines

The Australian/Vogel's Literary Award:
www.allenandunwin.com/being-a-writer/the-australian-vogel-s-literary-award

Note that Allen & Unwin only accepts manuscripts correctly submitted through their electronic system.

Amphorae Publishing Group

www.amphoraepublishing.com/about/

Romance, Sci fi, Historical Fiction, Novel, Literary Fiction, YA Fiction

Amphorae publishes works with a literary sensibility. Historical fiction, contemporary fiction, crime, mystery/thriller, literary, romance, memoir, and YA. While they indicate they are open to agented fiction, it might be worthwhile attending a writers' conference and arranging to make your pitch in person.

Amphorae Publishing is open to a wide variety of genres through each of their imprints:

- Blank Slate Press publishes works with a literary sensibility in Historical Fiction, Contemporary Fiction, Crime Fiction, Mysteries and Thriller Fiction, and Literary Fiction.
- Walrus Publishing seeks work that "pushes the envelope" and breaks new ground in science fiction/fantasy, relationship, memoir, regional, humor, and LGBTQ.
- Treehouse Publishing Group publishes children's books, picture books, middle grade, and young adult (fiction and nonfiction).

The bottom line is great writing, intriguing characters, and a little extra something to stand out in the crowd—even for nonfiction.

Amphorae seeks excellent writers who are committed to and excited about marketing their book, fostering their author presence online and off, and building a community of readers. Amphorae is a woman and veteran owned business.

They are also open to agented submissions. Contact Laura Robinson at acquisitions@amphoraepublishing.com. Amphorae is specifically seeking: Literary Fiction, Historical Fiction, Science Fiction, LGBTQ Fiction, and Mystery/Thrillers. They are not accepting queries for children's books or illustrated books.

Anaiah Press
submissions@anaiahpress.com
www.anaiahpress.com

Novella, Novel, Christian, New Writers

Anaiah Press is a POD, digital, and Christian publisher of fantasy, romance, sci fi, suspense/thriller fiction. Novella manuscripts should come in at 20-40,000 words, and novels between 40 to 100,000. Query with first 10 pages. Check their imprints for specific guidelines. They often post special calls for submission, such as for a Christmas issue, on their blog page.

Their goal is to provide their authors with the close-knit, hands-on experience of working with a small press, while making sure they don't have to sacrifice quality editing, cover art, and marketing. Authors who sign with Anaiah Press can expect:

- Release in digital and POD formats;
- An editor assigned to provide quality editing and to guide you every step of the way throughout the publication process;
- A marketing/publicity specialist who will create a marketing and publicity plan specific to your book;
- High-quality covers expertly designed specifically for your book;
- Royalties in the amount of 40% on net for digital format and 9-12% net on all other formats,

They do not accept proposals for works yet to be written. Only query them if your manuscript is complete.

As a Christian press, they publish books with a strong inspirational theme and/ or a message of faith. They do not accept manuscripts with the following:

- Anti-Christian propaganda/ themes
- Gratuitous sex/ sexual situations
- Messages of religious or social intolerance
- Angel/human or demon/human romantic relationships
- Werewolf, vampire, demon, etc. protagonists

To submit a manuscript for consideration, send a query letter and the first ten pages in the body of an e-mail to the e-mail address above.

Include the word "Query" and the title of your work in the subject line. They do respond personally to every query received. Allow 8 to 12 weeks for a response. Simultaneous submissions are fine, but they do ask that, out of professional courtesy, you let them know if you receive an offer from another publisher or agent.

Word count requirements are as follows:

- Anaiah Romance: 20,000–90,000
- Anaiah Surge: 50,000–90,000
- Anaiah Adventures: under 50,000 words

To determine which imprint is the right fit for your manuscript, visit their imprints page

Analog Science Fiction & Fact

44 Wall Street
Suite 904
New York, NY 10005-2401
www.analogsf.com/contact-us/writers-guidelines

Nonfiction, Flash Fiction, Poetry, Sci fi, New Writers

This is a good place to get a start in the sci fi world. They do not publish books, just shorter works that can help authors develop a publication record. They are a science fiction publisher of flash fiction, short stories, novelettes, and novellas. They provide professional payments for their authors.

Their online submissions form for fiction asks for your name, e-mail address, cover letter, story title, and story. Your cover letter should contain the length of your story, your publishing history, and any other relevant information (e.g., if you send them a story about a medical disaster and you happen to be an emergency room nurse, mention that). They ask for the same information for poetry. Include up to six poems in one submission for poetry, and wait until you have heard back on those before sending them more.

Anhinga Press

P.O. Box 10595
Tallahassee, FL 32302
www.anhingapress.org

Literary Contest, New Writers, Poetry, Chapbook

Anhinga Press publishes full-length collections of poetry (usually 60-80 pages). They publish three to four books a year. In the fall of 2015 they launched their first chapbook contest. The books they publish annually include:

- The winner of the Robert Dana-Anhinga Prize for Poetry (May 31 deadline)
- The Van K. Brock Florida Poetry Series
- The winner of the Philip Levine Prize in Poetry
- An occasional open-submission manuscript of the Directors' choice
- The Anhinga Press Chapbook Series

They seek to publish the best poetry by both emerging and established poets. Each of their contests requires a substantial entry fee, but winners receive a publishing contract and $2000 prize.

Antrim House

21 Goodrich Rd.
Simsbury, CT 06070-1804
eds@antrimhousebooks.com
(860) 217-0023
www.antrimhousebooks.com

New Writers, Memoirs, Novel, Poetry

Antrim House was founded in 1990 to promote the work of New England poets and has been especially active since 2001. Poets from New England and beyond who have produced a body of work sufficient to create a chapbook or full-length collection are invited to submit 3 poems (no more than 5 pages) as a sample.

Send your work with an e-mail address to the mailing address above. You will receive a response as quickly as possible, though your poems will not be returned. You may also submit your sample electronically to the e-mail address above.

Should your MS. be one of the few accepted for publication, the publisher (an award-winning author of many poetry collections) will be pleased to offer editorial advice and work with you to perfect your forthcoming book. And he will see to it that this book is a thing of beauty, working collaboratively with you concerning every aspect of the book's design, from cover to font selection and page layout. He will also be happy to assist in the selection of those whose comments appear on the back cover. You will never deal with an intern or an assistant, only with the publisher himself; and your book will never be allowed to go out of print.

Apex Press

Rowman & Littlefield
4501 Forbes Blvd.
Suite 200
Lanham, MD 20706
(301) 459-3366
www.rowman.com/Page/RLAuthRes

Nonfiction, Essays, International

Apex Press, established in 1990, is the imprint of a much larger company, Rowman & Littlefield, that is an academic and trade book publisher, Rowman & Littlefield Publishers. It was formerly an imprint of CIPA (Council on International and Public Affairs). The Council itself was founded in 1954 as a nonprofit human rights, education, research and publishing group.

The Apex Press publishes books to build democracy with equality — without which there can be no real democracy. This perspective shapes their work as an independent small publishing house. Their publishing program has a special focus on economic and social justice and world cultures. For submissions' instructions, see the weblink above. Go here for a list of their acquisition editors:

www.rowman.com/Page/RLPGAE

Aqueduct Press

Kathryn Wilham
info@aqueductpress.com
www.aqueductpress.com/submissions.php

Fiction, Novella, Novel, Literary Fiction, Sci fi

Aqueduct Press dedicates itself to publishing challenging, feminist science fiction. They promise to bring their readers work that will stretch the imagination and stimulate thought. Check their website for open submissions' periods.

The cover letter should be a brief introduction of yourself and your work to date; include your website or other web locations that showcase your work. Also, include a synopsis of the submission, not more than 2 pages single-spaced.

Arcade Publishing

307 West 36th Street
11th Floor
New York, NY 10018
(212) 643-6816
www.arcadepub.com/guidelines

Military, Creative Nonfiction, Fiction, Nonfiction, Story Collection, Novel

Arcade specializes in fiction, international fiction, military history, literary nonfiction, story collections, novels, and memoirs.

Send a query letter, synopsis and chapter outline, as well as a market analysis and sample chapters. They have a first class website and are open to receiving submissions for proposed books in the following categories:

- Adventure and Travel
- Fiction
- History
- Literary Nonfiction
- Military History
- Business
- Memoir
- Arts
- Nature and Science
- Food and Wine
- Current Events

Before submitting a proposal, they suggest that authors click around their site and take a look at the kinds of books they've published.

The Proposal
A strong book proposal consists of:

- A brief query (cover) letter
- A one-to-two page synopsis
- An annotated chapter outline

- Market analysis, including competitive research
- A sample chapter or two
- A curriculum vitae (bio) that includes a list of previous publishing credits

If they are interested in seeing more than the first 50 pages, they will contact you and request the balance of the manuscript.

Send all submissions to:

arcadesubmissions@skyhorsepublishing.com

If they are interested, they will get back to you within 4-6 weeks. Unfortunately, due to the volume of queries, they will not be able to respond to everyone. Do not mail hard copies or originals unless requested.

Arc Pair Press
www.arcpairpress.com/submissions.html

Novella, Creative Nonfiction, Nonfiction, Story Collection

APP's reading period is Feb. 1-May 1. They specialize in publishing mini books. There are no reading fees for submissions, but they'd love it if prospective authors bought a book. The manuscript length should fall between 60 and 120 pages. Send submissions to arcpairpress@gmail.com.

They offer two publishing options. The first option is the traditional chapbook publication. Print Copies: 150; Availability: Arc Pair Press Website; Author Payment: 25 Copies; Rights revert to the author after publication.

Their second option falls somewhere between traditional chapbook publishing and the publication of a full-length book. The mini-book will be available through print-on-demand distribution services, including Amazon and other retailers, with a Kindle e-book option, for a minimum of one-year. Print Copies: 1 Box for First Run (Approx. 100 copies) + Print-on-Demand; Additional copies will be printed to maintain stock until the termination of the contract. Availability: Arc Pair Press Website, Amazon, Wholesale Catalogues (for libraries/bookstores), and Others Kindle E-book Option; Author Payment: 25 Copies + Potential for Royalties + Discounts on Additional Copies; Rights revert to the author upon termination of the contract.

Arsenal Pulp Press

Brian Lam
#202 -211 East Georgia Street
Vancouver, BC
Canada V6A 1Z6
www.arsenalpulp.com/About-Arsenal-Pulp-Press/Submission-Guidelines

YA New Adult, YA Fiction, Canadian, Nonfiction, Children's Books, Literary Fiction, Novel

Arsenal Pulp Press specializes in the following:

- Regional nonfiction, particularly for British Columbia
- Literary Fiction and nonfiction (no genre fiction, such as mysteries, thrillers, or romance, but LGBTQ books are desirable)
- Graphic novels
- Youth culture and young adult literature
- Children's books with a diversity angle

Arsenal Pulp Press is a book publisher in Vancouver, Canada with over 300 titles currently in print, which include literary fiction and nonfiction; cultural and gender studies; LGBT and multicultural literature; cookbooks, including vegan; alternative crafts; graphic novels; visual arts; and books in translation. They are interested in literature that engages and challenges readers, and which asks probing questions about the world around them.

With a staff of five, located in the historic Vancouver district of Chinatown, they publish between 14 and 20 new titles per year, as well as an average of 12 to 15 reprints; their books are distributed in Canada, the U.S., Great Britain, Australia, and English-speaking Europe, and translations of their books have appeared in China, Japan, Taiwan, South Korea, France, Spain, Italy, German, Turkey, and Brazil.

Arte Público Press

submapp@uh.edu
www.artepublicopress.com/submissions/

Children's Books, Hispanic, Novel, Nonfiction, Poetry, Story Collection

Arte Público Press is the nation's largest and most established publisher of contemporary and recovery literature by U.S. Hispanic authors. Its imprint for children and young adults, Piñata Books, is dedicated to the realistic and authentic portrayal of the themes, languages, characters, and customs of Hispanic culture in the United States. Based at the University of Houston, Arte Público Press, Piñata Books and the Recovering the U.S. Hispanic Literary Heritage project provide a widely recognized and extensive showcase for Hispanic literary arts, history, and politics.

Arte Público Press, affiliated with the University of Houston, specializes in publishing contemporary novels, short stories, poetry, and drama based on U.S. Hispanic (Cuban American, Mexican American, Puerto Rican, and others) cultural issues and themes. Arte Público also is interested in reference works and nonfiction studies, especially of Hispanic civil rights, women's issues and history.

Manuscripts, queries, synopses, outlines, proposals, introductory chapters, etc. are accepted in either English or Spanish, although the majority of their publications are in English.

Response time is 2-4 months for queries and proposals and 3-6 months for manuscripts. Please use their submission form.

www.artepublicopress.com/manuscript-submissions-form/

Artemesia Publishing

9 Mockingbird Hill Rd
Tijeras, NM 87059
(505) 286-0892
info@artemesiapublishing.com
www.artemesiapublishing.com/forauthor.html

Children's Books, Nonfiction, Novella, YA Fiction

A small publisher for children's and YA books, Artemesia Publishing publishes nonfiction and fiction books for general audiences, both adults and children. They will consider proposals for projects in most genres, however they will not accept any work that contains erotica, sexually explicit, or other hard-core material. They will accept proposals for both adult books and children's books.

They accept only well-written, entertaining manuscripts that can capture a reader's attention. The book must be both informative and engaging to the reader, written in lively, lucid prose.

For nonfiction books the topic must have broad, long-term appeal. The sources authors rely on must be thoroughly documented and not infringe on any existing copyrights. Authors are responsible for supplying all photographs, maps, and other graphics the book may need.

For fiction books (including children's books) the story must be unique and engaging, capturing the reader's attention and not be something seen a thousand times before.

Ashton Publishing Group

www.ashtonpublishinggroup.com/submit-your-manuscript-to-a-publisher/

Thriller, Romance, Mystery, Crime, Novel

They are currently only accepting manuscripts from authors with multiple titles. At the moment, they are primarily looking at publishing novel length romance books, including all sub-genres of romance, such as contemporary romance, erotica, historical romance, new adult and college, and westerns. Occasionally they may accept shorter novellas as manuscripts in any of these categories. They will also consider novel length manuscripts in the thriller, crime, suspense, or mystery categories.

When authors first go shopping for a publisher, one of the first questions that gets asked is "Why are royalties calculated on the net amount, rather than the gross amount?" Well, there are certainly some publishers who use the "gross amount" process...but here's what they don't tell you.

If one form of advertising costs $1,000, and makes $1,500 in sales, there is $500 net profit. So the author gets $250, and the publisher get $250. Sounds perfectly fair and reasonable right?

But here's how it works out if the split is off the gross amount: The cost is $1,000, and makes $1,500. The publisher pays the $1,000, then the $1,500 is split 50/50, meaning $750 each.

Now the publisher has spent $1,000 to make $750, which means they have lost $250. If the publisher wants to stay in business, they are never going to do that promotion ever again. Why would they? They lose money every time they promote the book!

Changing to a split of net royalties makes the publisher driven to promote the book to the best of their abilities. Making the split of gross royalties can put the author and publisher in a situation where promotion becomes a disincentive, and that's not good for anyone.

Astrophil Press

Duncan Barlow
The University of South Dakota
Department of English
Dakota Hall, Room 212
414 E. Clark St.
Vermillion, SD 57069
www.astrophilpress.com/submissionguidelines-bedford

Literary Fiction, New Writers, Novel, Poetry, Literary Criticism

This publisher specializes in books from South Dakota. Astrophil Press does not read manuscripts outside of their open reading periods. All manuscripts will be handled through Submittable; the Submittable link will be available on this page during their open reading periods.

Note that this is the only way they consider work. They offer calls with particular requirements, so make sure your work/letter speaks to these specific requirements or prompts before sending your work. All manuscripts/letters that don't speak to the requirements will most likely not be considered.

They are dedicated to publishing innovative literary work. They publish work that is fertile in imagination and mind—literary art that many major presses and independent presses overlook. Astrophil is interested in writing that grows out of an understanding of its lineage and seeks to work out of that lineage by actively breaking boundaries.

What they publish:

- Fiction: Astrophil Press publishes fiction that defies genre, but does not ignore it. It is work that is at once playful but striking.
- Poetry: Astrophil Press focuses on poetry that tells a story either through image or sound. Poetry that does not try to disrupt, but teaches its readers how to read and participate in its journey.
- Critical: Astrophil Press is interested in Literary Criticism that focuses on contemporary authors or authors who have been overlooked by popular trends of the past and present.

Because of the volume of submissions they receive, reading can often take up to six months. However, the average response time is often three months or less. Check with your Submittable page to see the status of your manuscript. Though they wish they could respond to every submission personally, they cannot, but understand that they will read all work carefully and appreciate the time and energy you put into your work. If you have not received word on your submission after six months, you may contact them and inquire about your work. As a general rule, you attract more flies with honey than with vinegar.

Below is a link to their Submittable page.

www.astrophilpress.submittable.com/submit

Autonomous Press

nick@autpress.com
www.autpress.com/about-us/submissions-book-proposals/

Anthology, Memoirs, Literary Fiction, Novel, Creative Nonfiction

This is a press for authors who are neurodivergent, queer, transgender, mad, disabled, racialised, presently or formerly homeless or incarcerated, but that's not all they're about.

Autonomous Press publishes both fiction and nonfiction. Scholarly or journalistic works, novels, anthologies, and memoirs. They'll consider any genre, and they love innovative hybrid works that defy traditional genre categories.

They're looking for books that are, above all, transformative. Books that have the potential to expand minds, to introduce readers to radically new perspectives, to spark personal and cultural change. They want books that pose a danger to dominant paradigms, prejudices, and assumptions. Books that wake people up.

They do not publish work that promotes or reinforces societal systems of oppression such as racism, misogyny, homophobia, transphobia, or ableism.

Autonomous Press (also known as AutPress) is an independent publisher focusing on works about disability, neurodivergence, and the various ways they can intersect with other aspects of identity and lived experience. They are a partnership of disabled workers including writers, poets, artists, musicians, community scholars, and professors. Each partner takes on a share of the work of managing the press and production, and all of their workers are co-owners.

Autumn House Fiction and Poetry Contests

P.O. Box 60100
Pittsburgh, PA 15211
(412) 381-4261
rstjohn@autumnhouse.org
www.autumnhouse.org

Literary Contest, Novel, Nonfiction, Poetry

The annual Autumn House Press Contests award publication to full-length manuscripts in Poetry, Fiction, and Nonfiction. Each winner also receives $2,500 ($1,000 advance against royalties and a $1,500 travel/publicity grant to promote the book). The submission period opens January 1, and the postmark deadline for entries is June 30. To submit online, visit their online submission manager. Note that, at this time, Autumn House accepts unsolicited manuscripts only through these contests.

The Rising Writer Contest is for a first full-length book of poetry by an author 33 years old or younger. In addition to publication the winner also receives $1,000 ($500 advance against royalties and a $500 travel and publicity grant to promote the book). The submission period opens November 1, and the postmark deadline is January 31.

Though they are open to all styles of poetry, fiction, and nonfiction, they suggest you familiarize yourself with previous Autumn House publications before submitting. They are committed not just to publishing the prominent voices of their age, but also to publishing first books and lesser-known authors who will become the important writers of their generation.

Avon Romance

www.avonromance.com/impulse/

Novel, Romance, Mystery

Avon Romance publishes most subgenres in this highly popular field, including: Chick Lit, Contemporary, Erotic Romance, Historical, Paranormal, Romantic Suspense. Subscribe to their newsletter to learn about open submission periods.

Avon is looking for stories of emotional complexity, written by authors with unique voices. Books with humor, drama, suspense; with sizzling sensuality and irresistible characters—all types and tones can be right for Avon.

If your manuscript is exciting, electrifying, and exceptional, then they want to see it. Take them to the darkest depths or make them laugh out loud—everything is welcome! During their open submission periods, they're actively seeking all genres of romance of all lengths, including (but not limited to): historical, paranormal, contemporary, and erotica.

Ayin Press

Tom Haviv

tmhaviv@gmail.com

www.ayinpress.org/

Essays, Fiction, Nonfiction, Poetry, Art, Translation, Graphic novel

Ayin is an independent press (with a focus on Jewish culture) that publishes art books, books of poetry, anthologies, and works of nonfiction. They specialize in interdisciplinary work, speculative spirituality/theology, political imagination, work in translation, and work related to the Middle East and the Mediterranean. They operate a smaller imprint called "Somewhere" for children's books, graphic fiction and artists' books. Ayin is a letter in Arabic, Farsi, Hebrew, Phoenician, Urdu and many other languages. Ayin is also the word for eye.

Baen Books

www.baen.com/baen-faq#Manuscript Submission Guidelines

Fantasy, Publishers, Novel, Sci fi

They are looking for sci fi novels based on real science: 100,000 to 130,000 words. They publish only science fiction and fantasy.

Writers familiar with what they have published in the past will know what sort of material they are most likely to publish in the future: powerful plots with solid scientific and philosophical underpinnings are the *sine qua non* for consideration for science fiction submissions.

As for fantasy, any magical system must be both rigorously coherent and integral to the plot, and overall the work must at least strive for originality.

Those manuscripts that survive the "first cut" as outlined above are then judged primarily on plot and characterization. Style: Simple is generally better; in their opinion good style, like good breeding, never calls attention to itself.

Bancroft Press

Bruce Bortz
P.O. Box 65360
Baltimore, MD 21209-9945
www.bancroftpress.com/submission-guidelines-2

Nonfiction, Novel, Memoirs, Literary Fiction, Publishers

Bancroft publishes trade fiction and nonfiction, and they publish what they like, specifically, "Books that enlighten."

Virtually every genre is represented by one of their fine authors, from classic literature to political memoirs, from illustrated picture books to gripping suspense thrillers. The key is in the quality.

They ask for prospective authors' patience in waiting for their response. They do their best to respond within 6 months, but occasionally they are unable to do so. If an author would like a manuscript returned, include an appropriately sized envelope with correct postage. If an author prefers to have the manuscript recycled, say so in the cover letter.

There is no need to send submissions priority mail, FedEx, overnight, etc. They receive many submissions each day, and the expedience with which the manuscript arrives does not affect the expedience with which it is read.

Mark your shipment appropriately, e.g., fiction or nonfiction.

Baobab Press

Attn: Acquisitions Editor
121 California Avenue
Reno, NV 89509
(775) 786-1188
www.baobabpress.com/submissions/

Novel, Poetry, Creative Nonfiction, Comic/Visual Narrative

Baobab Press constantly strives to discover, cultivate, and nurture authors working in all genres. They have a special fondness for Nevada-based books.

They believe in the importance of collaboration between author and publisher and seek to establish long-term relationships with their authors, providing them with the support necessary to see their works of art reach their fullest potential and widest readership. Their goal is to help their authors grow books that resonate today and will continue to be vital in the years to come.

Baobab Press shares the Levy Mansion with Sundance Books and Music, and they are located in Reno, Nevada. Their books are distributed by Publishers Group West.

Authors are requested to send the following:

- Brief Bio
- Synopsis (300 words or fewer)
- Sample (up to 25 double-spaced pages)

Send print submissions to the address above. Include a self-addressed stamped envelope.

Send Digital Submissions in the following format: Subject line: Your Name, Title of Work, Genre (example: Stephen King, The Shining, Fiction).

For digital submissions, use their Submittable portal, and enter your bio, synopsis, and sample into the body of the e-mail.

www.baobabpress.submittable.com/submit

Barrow Street Press Book Contest

P.O. Box 1831
New York, NY 10156
www.barrowstreet.org/press/submit

Literary Contest, Poetry

The Barrow Street book contest deadline ends on June 30th. Use their Online Submission Manager to submit.

The Barrow Street Press Book Contest award will be given for the best previously unpublished manuscript of poetry in English. The winner will receive book publication by Barrow Street Press and $1,500.

Beacon Press

24 Beacon Street
Boston, MA 02108
(617) 742-2110
editorial@beacon.org
www.beacon.org

Creative Nonfiction, Essays Memoirs, Nonfiction

Prospective authors who would like Beacon Press to consider their work should first familiarize themselves with the company's mission statement and current publications' list. Note that they are not accepting submissions for new poetry, fiction, or self-help books at this time, and will not review, respond to, or return submissions of this type.

Also note that their publishing mission is currently general trade; some of their publications are trade books with an additional scholarly market. They are not currently accepting submissions for purely academic projects. See their current catalogue to determine if your manuscript is a good fit.

Authors who believe their work would be a good fit should e-mail a 250-word query describing their proposal to editorial@beacon.org. If they are interested in receiving a full proposal, they will respond within three weeks. If not, authors will not receive a response.

Beaufort Books

info@beaufortbooks.com
www.beaufortbooks.com/contact/submission-guidelines/

Memoirs, Literary Fiction, Nonfiction, New Writers, Fiction, Novel

Beaufort Books is a general interest adult fiction and nonfiction publisher, and they are looking for material that reflects that focus. Also, be aware that they do not give advances for work and prefer to work with manuscripts that are complete or near completion.

Digital submissions are the only way potential authors can submit. All submissions are accepted through their portal at Submittable. Simply click on that link, follow directions, fill out the forms and upload the typed manuscript and supporting materials in PDF file format. They do not accept hard copy, faxed, or on-disk submissions.

www.beaufortbooks.submittable.com/submit

Authors should include a cover letter with a brief bio and description of how they came to write the book. Also, send:

- A synopsis. Keep it direct, simple, and under one page.
- The target audience for your book and how the book appeals to that market.
- A list of relevant corporate or media contacts that would help in the promotion and publicity of the book.
- Contact details.
- A minimum of three sample chapters or the full manuscript. No short stories or erotica.

Bella Books

P.O. Box 10543
Tallahassee, FL 32302
(800) 729-4992
submissions@bellabooks.com
www.bellabooks.com

LGBQ, Novel

At Bella Books, they believe stories about lesbians are an essential of life—and so do their readers. They are interested in acquiring manuscripts that tell terrific stories about lesbians. Love, life, adventure, drama—they're looking for imaginative and entertaining stories that illuminate and celebrate their realities and fantasies.

They also believe that their readers have high standards for exciting, fresh plots, and that they relish hours spent with engaging characters whose complexities, struggles and triumphs celebrate their hopes and dreams. They want books they can't put down, stories they think about for days afterward, and characters so compelling they wish they could meet them.

To provide their readers with the kinds of stories they demand and deserve, they publish general lesbian fiction, romance, mystery, action/thriller, science-fiction, fantasy, and erotica. No need for an agent at this time.

Belle Lutte Press

Inquiries@BelleLutte.com

www.bellelutte.com/catalogue-of-works/

Novel, Sci fi

This is a new press, publishing two books a year.

An Acadian press, rooted in Louisiana, Belle Lutte Press's mission is to bring exceptionalism back to the masses. While today's media maximizes profits by force-feeding the populace cheap and unoriginal thought, Belle Lutte Press is fighting the good fight—hell-bent on publishing original, high-quality novels.

Belle Lutte (pronounced "bell loot") translates to "Good Fight" and "Beautiful Struggle" in French—ideas integral to the Press's mission. The name is also an homage to the term *belles-lettres*, a French phrase meaning "fine writing." Query them via e-mail.

Bellevue Literary Press

Erika Goldman, Publisher and Editorial Director
Dept. of Medicine
NYU School of Medicine
550 First Ave., OBV 612
New York, NY10016
blpsubmissions@gmail.com
www.blpress.org/contact/

Literary Fiction, Creative Nonfiction, Essays, Fiction, Nonfiction

Highly competitive, Bellevue Literary Press publishes literary fiction and narrative nonfiction geared toward a general readership. They do not publish poetry, single short stories, plays, screenplays, memoir, or self-help/instructional books. If you are unsure whether your manuscript would be a good fit for their list, you may send a query e-mail, using the same subject line as for a submission.

E-mail all submissions to blpsubmissions@gmail.com with the subject line in this format: TITLE OF MANUSCRIPT — AUTHOR'S LAST NAME — MM/DD/YY.

In the body of the e-mail, include a comprehensive cover letter with a description of the manuscript and biographical information.

- For fiction submissions, attach the full manuscript. Excerpts will not be accepted.
- For nonfiction submissions, attach the full manuscript or a formal proposal. A synopsis is recommended but not required.

If an author's submission meets their guidelines, they will be in touch as soon as they reach a decision, but if they're not interested, authors will not hear back.

Bellwether Prize/PEN

588 Broadway, Suite 303
New York, NY 10012
www.pen.org/literary-award/penbellwether-prize-for-socially-engaged-fiction-25000

Literary Fiction, Literary Contest, Novel, New Writers

Highly competitive, the PEN/Bellwether Prize for Socially Engaged Fiction was founded by author Barbara Kingsolver. Submissions for their award cycle are accepted from June 1 through October 26.

The Bellwether Prize, which was established in 2000 by Barbara Kingsolver and is funded entirely by her, was created to promote fiction that addresses issues of social justice and the impact of culture and politics on human relationships. The $25,000 prize is awarded biennially to the author of a previously unpublished novel of high literary caliber that exemplifies the prize's founding principles. The winner also receives a publishing contract with Algonquin Books. Eligible authors must be U.S. citizens.

Biblioasis

1520 Wyandotte Street East
Windsor, ON
Canada N9A 3L2
info@biblioasis.com
www.biblioasis.com/

Story Collection, Novel, Nonfiction, Memoirs, Literary Fiction, Anthology, Canadian

Biblioasis is an award-winning independent publishing house based in Windsor, Ontario. They publish approximately 25 titles a year, including short fiction, novels, poetry, literary criticism, memoir, *belles lettres*, local and regional history, and general nonfiction.

They do publish American writers, but require that you send the manuscript. If this is an unsolicited submission, mark the envelope with the phrase "Press Submissions," and the genre (i.e., fiction, short fiction, poetry, memoir, etc.).

Include an introductory letter that describes the work and compares it to at least two current Biblioasis titles, explaining what the book will contribute to the publisher's list. Include a literary curriculum vitae listing previous publications and all relevant experience.

Big Table Publishing

Robin Stratton

www.bigtablepublishing.com/submission-guidelines

Poetry, Nonfiction, Story Collection, Novel, Literary Fiction, Memoir

BTP is looking for well-written, high-quality manuscripts in the following genres: novels, poetry, short fiction, memoirs, history, political, self-help/motivational, biography, science, social studies, philosophy, psychology, and young adult (fiction and nonfiction.) They are not interested in graphic novels, children's books, oversized coffee table books with color images, fantasy, books about vampires or zombies, or erotica.

While they are a traditional royalty-paying press and never charge for editing or publishing, they do require a minimum purchase of 65 copies upon publication. They also require that authors have a professional website to sell their book online and a PayPal account to receive royalty payments.

Authors significantly improve their chance of receiving an invitation to send a writing sample if the query includes the following:

NONFICTION

- An irresistible, brilliantly-crafted tagline
- An author's biography/credentials
- A Table of Contents with chapter/section titles
- For science, medical, or political manuscripts, authors must include a list of qualified people they expect to worked with or contact, and a list of publications that will be cited.

FICTION:

- A single paragraph synopsis
- A chapter by chapter outline

POETRY AND SHORT STORY COLLECTIONS

- Query only

WITH ALL SUBMISSIONS

- Genre
- Word count
- A link to the author's professional website
- A detailed marketing plan that demonstrates an understanding of the market/audience, and the author's willingness to work hard to promote the book

The publisher is affiliated with the Newton Writing & Publishing Center in Boston.

Big Wonderful Press

www.bigwonderfulpress.com/become-a-wonderful-author/

YA Fiction, Anthology, Fiction, Novel, Chapbook

Big Wonderful Press is a traditional publisher. They publish using both POD and traditional print runs, depending on the book, and they also publish e-books. They also market their books and provide full editing and design. They accept unsolicited submissions only during their open submissions' periods, and these are generally focused on a specific theme.

If a prospective author purchases one of the company's chapbooks, then that author may submit a manuscript for consideration. Fiction chapbooks must be more than one story or flash piece and less than 40 pages long. The online purchase requirement serves two purposes: it prevents too many low-quality submissions, and it helps gain a wider audience for the author.

There is another way to work with this publisher, and that is by creating and editing an anthology. Submit the idea and proposed process, as well as a resume. The editor will be paid in royalties, copies, and swag. Note, an anthology means the work of multiple authors. Single author collections will not be considered.

Submit your poetry or fiction chapbook and purchase *Something Impossible Happens* or *Bain Marie* (at a big discount!) in one step (free shipping in the U.S.; include address on the cover letter) for a limited time.

Big Yes Press

San Luis Obispo, CA 94304
www.bigyespress.com/

Literary Fiction, Poetry, Essays, Short stories

BYP serves every book with care. This can take months, start to release, so if an author is in a hurry, consider other options. BYP makes no money from the sale of BYP books. They are writers and poets who do this because they want to do this! All BYP books have a print run of in-the-hand books, using production partners that beat Amazon for high quality and cost. BYP is committed to authors retaining 100% ownership and 100% of the profits from the sale of their books. There is no pre-order or minimum copies sold.

Unsolicited queries from established and emerging writers and poets are welcome. Have a titled, complete book-length (minimum of 55-60 pages for poetry, longer in other genres) manuscript of ordered poetry or writing ready to submit. No chapbooks. Collections of short fiction or graphic poetry will be considered.

When ready, e-mail BYP at plbigyes@gmail.com with a query that includes: a brief book synopsis, short bio, and 3-5 poem sample or first chapter. A prospective author's letter should include information about how they heard about BYP and why they want to publish with BYP. The publisher hopes to see that the author is publishing in literary journals, reading in their community, and joining with other writers in critique. They want to hear how authors are involved in passions that feed your writing. And, this part is important: Tell them who you want to have read your book and how you intend to promote your book to reach those readers. Books in boxes are a loss to readers. BYP wants books in hand!

BYP will let a prospective author know if the query sparks interest and will pass the query around so that their editors can read it and then meet to talk about the manuscript. They will provide the author with feedback from their discussion as a courtesy (no form letters). If it's a match, they will then talk about next steps.

Kindly do not send a manuscript in whole or part until you have introduced yourself and your book to BYP and gotten an invitation to start a dialogue to see if your book is a fit.

Birds LLC

Dan Boehl, Founding Editor
(443) 362-8124
dboehl@gmail.com
www.birdsllc.com/

Poetry

Submissions are by request. Query first. Birds, LLC is a small, independent poetry press based out of Minneapolis, New York, and Raleigh.

Founded in 2009 as a poetry publisher that would take an active role in editing and marketing the work of talented writers, Birds, LLC was conceived as an organization that rejects the morass of first book contests and the disinterested marketing style of university presses.

Birds, LLC strives to find innovative manuscripts from talented writers and specializes in close author relationships. They believe great books are the result of productive collaborations between editors and authors. Birds, LLC is committed to diversity and representing minority voices in the poetry marketplace.

BkMk Press

University of Missouri-Kansas City
5101 Rockhill Road
Kansas City, MO 64110-2499
(816) 235-2558
www.newletters.org/writers-wanted/BkMk-submissions

Poetry, Story Collection, Creative Nonfiction

BkMk publishes quality poetry, short fiction collections, and creative nonfiction essays. They do not currently publish novels. Their two contests have been running for many years and result in authors having a book contract and guarantee of publication.

BkMk Press typically reads unsolicited submissions from February 1 through June 30, using their Submittable portal. You can learn more about the contests and submission process there.

www.bkmkpress.submittable.com/submit

The submission deadline for the John Ciardi Prize for Poetry and the G. S. Sharat Chandra Prize for Short Fiction occurs annually on January 15.

Black Balloon Publishing

www.blackballoonpublishing.com/

Poetry, Graphic Novels, Memoirs, Novel

Experimental, literary, and quirky, this publisher is looking for unconventional artists, innovative writers, and the occasional digital delight.

They are big into graphic novels and quirky humor. Black Balloon's titles push the boundaries of what a book can be—from graphic novels to experimental writing to limited edition art books to digital projects and beyond. They champion the unconventional and believe in the meaningful above all.

Black Balloon is a critically acclaimed imprint of Catapult, an independent publishing company headquartered in New York, NY. Their books have been featured in *The New York Times Book Review, The New Yorker, O: The Oprah Magazine, Esquire, The Los Angeles Times, The Boston Globe, Wired.com, New York Magazine, The Atlantic, Time, Bon Appetit,* and on NPR's "All Things Considered," among many other outlets.

They accept unagented submissions twice yearly via Submittable. Please include a cover letter that explains (specifically) why your book is a good fit for Black Balloon.

www.catapult.submittable.com/submit

Black Heron Press
P.O. Box 614
Anacortes, WA 98221
www.blackheronpress.com/contact/

Literary Fiction, Novel, Story Collection

Black Heron Press is a literary press located in Seattle, Washington. Their authors have won some impressive awards. Literary Fiction only.

They distribute through Independent Publishers Group (IPG). Their books are also available from Ingram, Baker and Taylor, and most regional wholesalers. Black Heron Press prints 4-6 books a year. They publish primarily literary fiction.

They do not accept e-mailed submissions or queries. Prospective authors must mail their queries. Send to the address above:

- a one-page cover letter, including the manuscript's word count;
- the first 30-40 pages (they publish books only, not individual stories);
- an SASE.

Black Lawrence Press

8405 Bay Parkway
Suite C8
Brooklyn, NY 11214
www.blacklawrence.com/submissions-and-contests/the-st-lawrence-book-award/

Literary Fiction, Story Collection, Novel, Literary Contest

This publisher runs various book contests with deadlines spread throughout the year. Black Lawrence Press seeks to publish intriguing books of literature and creative nonfiction: novels, memoirs, short story collections, poetry, biographies, cultural studies, and translations from the German and French.

    www.blacklawrencepress.submittable.com/submit

Beginning with the 2014 St. Lawrence Book Award competition, all entries were read blind by their panel of editors. Manuscripts should include a title page (listing only the title of the work), table of contents, and when appropriate, an acknowledgments page.

Manuscripts should be 45-95 pages in length (poetry) or 120-280 pages in length (fiction), not including front and back matter (table of contents, title page, etc.). Identifying information for the author should not be included anywhere on the manuscript itself. Writers with MFAs (Masters' degrees in Creative Writing) often publish with this press.

Black Rose Writing

Reagan Rothe
www.blackrosewriting.com/submissions/

Children's Books, Fantasy, Romance, Novel, Thriller, Nonfiction, Memoir

This publisher would be receptive to authors of action-adventure, fantasy, horror, romance, suspense/thriller, true crime, sports, and much more.

Black Rose Writing is an independent publishing house that strongly believes in developing a personal relationship with their authors. The Texas-based publishing company doesn't see authors as clients or just another number on a page, but rather as individual people who deserve an honest review of their material and to be paid traditional royalties without ever paying any fees to be published.

Writers the publisher likes are Stephen King, Mario Puzo, George RR Martin, and Cormac McCarthy. The ideal submission is a well-written query with synopsis and author bio covering a story that is very unique and untold, with a strong title.

BlazeVOX Books

editor@blazevox.org
www.blazevox.org/

Story Collection, Novel, Poetry, Nonfiction, Literary Criticism

BlazeVOX [books] presents innovative fictions and wide ranging fields of contemporary poetry. Their books push at the frontiers of what is possible in innovative poetry, fiction and select nonfiction and literary criticism. Their fundamental mission is to disseminate poetry, through print and digital media, both within academic spheres and to society at large.

They seek to publish the innovative works of the greatest minds writing poetry today, from the most respected senior poets to extraordinarily promising young writers. They select for publication only the highest quality of writing on all levels, regardless of commercial viability. Their outlets of publication strive to enrich cultural and intellectual life and foster regional pride and accomplishments.

Manuscripts must conform to one criterion: the work must not suck. This put plainly, bad art should be punished; they will not promote it. However, all submissions will be reviewed, and the author will receive feedback.

Please send the manuscript to editor@blazevox.org as an attachment in either a Microsoft Word DOC, RTF, or even a PDF.

BLF

Stephanie Andrea Allen, Publisher
(706) 254-9582
s.andrea.allen@blfpress.com
www.blfpress.com

Essays, Memoir, Nonfiction, Poetry

BLF Press is an independent Black feminist press dedicated to amplifying the work of women of color. Their goal is to create a space for forward thinking, creative women of exceptional talent. They embrace difference and envision BLF Press as an outlet for the expression of various types of writing that address the experiences of women of color in the United States.

They are open to various types of literary work, including science fiction and shorter pieces that might be included in an anthology. While they welcome all submissions that meet their guidelines, they are especially interested in work that centers women, particularly women of color and same gender loving women. Their preferred genres are literary fiction, memoir, creative nonfiction, and short fiction. See their website for details.

Bloomsday Literary

Kate Martin Williams, Publisher
(713) 213-2178
kate@bloomsdayliterary.com
www.bloomsdayliterary.com

Literary Fiction, Young Adult, Nonfiction, Poetry, Essays

Their submission portal is open from June 1 to Dec 31 of every year. Writers submit using their online form and may choose to attach their full manuscript. The publisher asks that authors submit information regarding their existing platform and venues of previous publication.

www.form.jotform.com/81154917279162

Bloomsday Literary are publishers of literature. Unconfined by the limitations of bigger publishing houses to sell that which will net the most profits, Bloomsday gets to be nimbler and take greater risks, bringing more diverse voices to a more diverse readership. Bloomsday readers want books that change us, reorder our thinking, and make us feel hopeful about what good literature can accomplish in the world.

They do not enter the marketplace blindly, believing that books can exist on good writing alone, shorn of any interest in their marketability, but believing that the two—good writing and marketability—are symbiotic. Mindfully driven, it is the publisher's business to find readers for the writers they champion.

In a crowded cultural landscape increasingly governed by rancor and bombast ("full of sound and fury, signifying nothing"), at Bloomsday curiosity is their highest governing principle and their greatest refuge. This principle is made manifest through the following objectives: Give readers something beautiful, curious, life-changing, and life affirming.

Blue Skirt Press

www.blueskirtproductions.com/submissions

New Writers, Novella, Novel, Literary Magazine

Portland-based Blue Skirt Productions LLC seeks to publish and promote Gut Punch Fiction: emotional, philosophical, and transgressive works of literary fiction that punch the reader in the gut. They encourage diversity, hard-hitting works, and a strong sense of community. *Microfiction Monday Magazine* invites submissions of 100 words or less and is a way for authors to get a foot in the door.

They may be a small press, but Blue Skirt publishers give each manuscript they acquire their full attention and expertise when it comes to editing, book and cover design, and distribution. They also work with their authors to arrange speaking/reading engagements and other publicity.

If you have a novella or novel you would like them to consider for publication, send a query, short synopsis, and the first five pages (during open submissions) to Submissions@BlueSkirtProductions.com. In the subject line of your e-mail, write "Press Submission: (title of manuscript)".

BOA Short Fiction Prize

American Reader Series
260 N. Goodman Street
Suite 306
Rochester, NY 14607
(585) 546-3410
www.boaeditions.org/

Story Collection, Fiction, Poetry, Literary Contest

Submit to their fiction contest April 1-May 31. They like short, short fiction. In spring of the year following the competition, BOA editions will give the contest winner a published book and a $1,000 honorarium.

Since its founding in 2010, the BOA Short Fiction prize has been awarded to six of the most exciting and unique voices in American fiction. As with all BOA fiction titles, their prize-winning short story collections are more concerned with the artfulness of writing than the twists and turns of plot. It is their belief that short story writing is a valuable and underserved literary form that they are proud to support, nurture, and celebrate.

They also have the A. Poulin, Jr. Poetry Prize, awarded to a poet's first book and with a $1000 prize, plus publication.

Submissions are invited only through Submittable or by post mail. They do not have the staff capacity to read or respond to manuscripts that are submitted by fax or e-mail. Note that submission fees allow them to offer a $1,000 honorarium and also offset the cost of publishing and promoting the winning collection. To enter, an author must be a U.S. resident.

www.boaeditions.submittable.com/submit

Bookouture

www.submit.bookouture.com/submit/72839/submit-your-manuscript?utm_source=website&utm_medium=about-button

Women's Fiction, Historical Fiction, Novel, Sci fi, Thriller

Bookouture is a digital imprint offering big publisher expertise, small publisher flexibility, and great royalties. According to the publisher, they publish great books, build author brands, and create smart, effective marketing plans.

They focus on a small number of books—because attention to detail is essential. They want each of their authors to be a bestseller—so they treat them like one.

The company CEO is the former head of social media, digital marketing and publishing at Harlequin, U.K., Oliver Rhodes. Authors receive a 45% of net receipts royalty in e-books, and they produce POD print books. They have a unique book production and marketing philosophy called Bespoke Publishing, meaning that their marketing is targeted to an author's brand, not the other way around.

The publisher is based in Great Britain and is highly involved in digital marketing. Their services are similar to those provided by SheWrites Press in that authors can choose from a menu of book-production services that includes formatting and book production, as well as marketing. Like vanity presses, this publisher charges money up front for some of their services.

Bottom Dog Press

Larry Smith
P.O. Box 425
Huron, OH 44839
Lsmithdog@smithdocs.net
www.smithdocs.net/submission_guidelines

Poetry, Memoirs, New Writers, Novel

Due to increased costs and decreased funding, Bottom Dog is now asking that you include a "reader's fee" of $20.

They are a book publisher; they do not accept individual poems, stories, or essays unless for a specific collection for which they have sent out a call (e.g. working-class short stories or family poems for an announced anthology).

They require that you submit a query first, that you write out a description of your book yourself (as writer and person), explaining the potential audience for that book. Where are you from, what have you done, what are your plans for this book? You may include a few poems, a sample essay, or a story to introduce yourself and the book. This may be done via e-mail.

As one of thousands of independent small presses, they have developed and achieved a certain character. In brief, they publish books focusing on these themes:

- Sense of Place (ie. the Midwest and Appalachia)
- Working-Class Culture and Values
- American Zen Writing
- African-American Writing from the Midwest
- Literary Biography
- Family and Spirit
- Peace and Justice.

They publish about 4-5 books a year of literary and social worth.

Braddock Avenue Books

P.O. Box 502
Braddock, PA 15104
braddockavenuebooks@gmail.com
www.braddockavenuebooks.com

Essays, Story Collection, Novel

Braddock Avenue Books is an independent literary publisher looking for works that speak to the difficulties and rewards of being human. They prefer fiction in a realistic mode and favor serious long-form essays that engage with contemporary circumstances in a style aimed at an educated, but not necessarily academic, audience.

They read submissions year-round. Manuscripts should not have been previously published, but excerpts can be. They accept simultaneous submissions, but let them know if accepted elsewhere.

- Novels: send 1) the cover letter and 2) the first chapter or up to 50 pages.
- Short Story Collections: send 1) the cover letter and 2) three stories.
- Nonfiction: send 1) the cover letter and 2) up to 40 pages by going to their submissions page.

www.braddockavenuebooks.com/submit

Brandt Street Press

Editor
5885 Bartlett Street
Pittsburgh, PA 15217
www.brandtstreetpress.com/submissions.html

Nonfiction, Memoirs, Novel, Literary Fiction, Creative Nonfiction

Their mission is to make history fun. Brandt Street Press is also looking for manuscripts that tell interesting stories from the past, whether it's an author's own past or somebody else's. Submissions may be nonfiction, memoir or fiction. If the submission's portal is full, sign up for their e-mail list so they can notify you when it reopens.

When it does, ask yourself these questions before you submit: Did I have fun writing this book? Is the language I use interesting? Do people enjoy reading it? If I was having dinner with a group of friends and told a story from this book, would it prompt laughter, fascination or a lively discussion?

If your answer to these questions is yes, consider submitting to them. If the book is academic in nature, or if it is filled with dates and statistics, they are probably not the publisher for you.

When open, they accept submissions of 35,000-100,000 words (140-400 pages). They typically reply within one to two months. Send a query letter with sample chapters (preferably first chapter and one or two others) to the editor at editor@brandtstreetpress.com. If they are not open, do not send a manuscript. Simultaneous submissions are fine.

Brash Books
www.brash-books.com/about/

New Writers, Novel, Mystery, Thriller

Check to see if they're open for submissions. To have your crime novel considered for publication, submit two chapters of your manuscript (double-spaced and not to exceed 25 pages), along with a synopsis (double-spaced and not to exceed two pages) by e-mail to brashbooks@gmail.com. They accept electronic submissions of Microsoft Word documents or PDF documents only. They'll contact the author or the agent to request a complete manuscript if they like what they read.

They publish the best crime novels in existence. Their award-winning, critically acclaimed authors prove it with each and every one of their amazing books. They've got it all: psychological thrillers, murder mysteries, international espionage, and police procedurals from established masters of the craft—as well as premier books from new voices who are sure to become crime fiction stars. If an aspiring author has great literary credentials, it might be worth looking for a conference where one of their editors is speaking and/or hosting a pitch session.

Breakaway Books

P.O. Box 24
Halcottsville, NY 12438
breakawaybooks@gmail.com
www.breakawaybooks.com

Poetry, Nonfiction, Essays, Novel

Breakaway Books publishes literary and thoughtful writing on sports — fiction, poetry, and essays on the athletic experience. They are interested in the emotional and metaphysical side of sports, the inner life of the athlete. They also celebrate the many ways sport can serve as muse for excellent writing — both serious and playful.

They also have a separate list of boatbuilding and boating books, with a soft spot for small craft, mostly paddle and sail. If an author wishes to submit writing to them for possible publication, send a query letter first.

They receive dozens of queries a day and more excellent manuscripts than they could ever publish. If it takes them a long time to respond, accept their apologies. Simultaneous submissions to other publishers are encouraged.

Brick Mantel Books

4719 Holly Hills Ave.
St. Louis, MO 63116
info@brickmantelbooks.com
www.brickmantelbooks.com/query.php

YA Fiction, New Adult, New Writers, Novel, Literary Fiction, Poetry

Subscribe to their newsletter for notification of their open reading periods. Brick Mantel Books publishes quality literary fiction and poetry. Their goal is to help readers gain a stronger sense of the world and humanity through literature.

If an author has written literary fiction that is character-driven, engaging, provocative, lyrical, artistic, experimental, or out-of-the-ordinary, or else contemporary and innovative poetry, query them.

When they are open, they accept full-length novels (preferably between 60,000 and 130,000 words) and poetry books (between 40 and 80 poems suggested).

Bright Hill Press

Bright HIll Press Poetry Chapbook Competition
P.O. Box 193
Treadwell, NY 13846-0193
wordthur@stny.rr.com
www.brighthillpress.org/submissionguidelines

Chapbook, Literary Contest, Poetry

Their poetry chapbook competition has a December 31 deadline. Poets wishing to enter the contest should do the following:

- Send 48-64 pages, plus bio, table of contents, acknowledgments page, and title page. Include two title pages: one with title only; one with title, author's name, address, and telephone. (Poems may be published in journals or anthologies; attach acknowledgments page to title page with author's name, address, and telephone.)
- Manuscripts will not be returned; include an SASE for results only.

Simultaneous submissions are acceptable, but Bright Hill Press must be notified if the manuscript is taken elsewhere. Follow the directions for paying the contest submission fee on their submissions' page above.

Broadstone Books

418 Ann Street
Frankfort, KY 40601-1929
(502) 223-4415
BroadstoneMedia@aol.com
www.broadstonebooks.com/Submission_Policy.html

Poetry, New Writers, Novel, Publishers

This publisher considers work in most genres; however, they do not publish children's literature, self-help, spiritualism, erotica or technical and professional subject matter. They love poetry, but they have their own editorial prejudices, and suggest that you read some of the books they've published to get a sense for what appeals to them.

They favor narrative poetry (e.g., Potter, Cimprich) and verse that treats the human condition with compelling language and imagery (e.g., Greene, Cope). They almost never publish verse that is overtly sexual, self-therapeutic, or too self-consciously about poets writing poetry. For fiction, they place a premium on careful use of language, and they are highly selective.

For the Broadstone Books Thomas Merton Series, they are pleased to consider new manuscripts that explore aspects of Merton's life and work that have been under-represented in the voluminous Mertonian literature.

Burrow Press

www.burrowpress.com

Nonfiction, Poetry, Story Collection, Novel

This Central-Florida-based literary arts organization has a small press component.

For a limited time beginning in February, Burrow considers agented and unagented submissions. They'll have categories open for novels, story collections, essays collections and memoirs. Special consideration will be given to underrepresented Florida authors and/or books that tackle Florida themes and places in a literary light.

Despite their broad "literary" preference, they welcome experimental styles, and if authors take a look at their current catalog, they'll notice their penchant for the weird (magic realism, absurdism, dark humor, etc). www.burrowpress.submittable.com/submit/52635/fantastic-floridas-fiction

C & R Press

www.crpress.org
www.crpress.submittable.com/submit

Poetry, Essays, Story Collection, Nonfiction, Literary Contest, Novel, Memoirs, Creative Nonfiction

This small press is looking for great short stories and amazing novels, by both new and established writers, to publish as C&R Fiction. Their award-winning fiction titles feature a range of voices and approaches that push boundaries, and their editorial focus is on strong writing.

The press got its start by publishing poetry, and they are still committed to publishing vibrant and dynamic poets—not only because they love the well-crafted line, but because they believe that poetry is the heartbeat of American culture.

Concept-driven nonfiction and creative nonfiction with a strong point of view are also works they're interested in seeing. Visionary writers, disruptive ideas, and hope for the future will capture their interest.

C&R Press is open for submissions of full-length manuscripts in every category. Novels, poetry, short story collections, creative nonfiction, memoir, essay, experimental and hybrid works are all considered, and they've published multiple books in each genre. All in all, they've published over 60 books and 12 chapbooks. Please see their submissions portal above for more information on their contests, each of which has a $1000 prize.

Candlemark & Gleam

www.candlemarkandgleam.com/about/submissions-2

Novella, Novel, Sci fi, Literary Fiction

Candlemark & Gleam publishes by invitation and referral, but they also accept unsolicited submissions. Unagented submissions are not merely fine but encouraged.

Long works: They're looking for completed, polished, novel-length work (~65K and up), prose only, primarily science fiction. They are also interested in collections of linked stories (for example, within a secondary science-fictional universe). Long works will be published in both print and digital format, and will have a professionally commissioned cover.

Medium works: They will also consider novelette/novella-length works, prose or poetry (12-42K) for their new imprint, The Reckless. These will be published exclusively in digital format, on the C&G website and on Amazon, and will have one of several professionally designed "concept" covers that fits their subgenre and content. (There will be an option for individualized covers as well.) Their royalties' structure will be identical to that of the longer works.

Content: Speculative fiction, broadly defined. Cross-genre/interstitial and SF/F hybrid works are fine, ones with mythic/historical echoes even better. Note that they want to see works by adults for adults (not teen or children's fiction). Works whose content is solely explicit erotica and stories whose main trope is horror will be a hard sell.

Carbon Books
www.carbonculturereview.com/carbonbooks

New Writers, Memoirs, Literary Fiction, Novel, Poetry

Carbon Books is the book arm of *Carbon Culture Review*, the internationally circulated newsstand magazine. Carbon Books is looking for fiction, poetry, memoir, and essay from every school of thought and practice. They plan to publish books that have a voice and are well crafted on any subject or theme.

They encourage new and established writers to submit their manuscripts during the open reading period. Authors will receive a standard royalty-based contract, promotion in each *Carbon Culture* newsstand edition, numerous review copies mailed to magazines and journals, and receive 15 copies of the finished book. They'll also host several readings for their authors at industry events.

They will be publishing 4-8 books in their first year and look forward to seeing what prospective authors submit.

www.carbonculturereview.submittable.com/submit

Carnegie Mellon University Press

Carnegie Mellon University
5032 Forbes Avenue
Pittsburgh, PA 15289-1021
cmupress@andrew.cmu.edu.
www.cmu.edu/universitypress

Essays, History, Nonfiction, Creative Nonfiction, Plays

The CMU Press publishes regional social history (titles that explore the rich history of Pittsburgh and Western Pennsylvania), art history, the performing arts (original plays and adaptations), literary analysis, education, and university history.

They consider manuscripts only during the month of October. Submissions are by e-mailed to the address above and should include the words "Nonfiction Submission" in the subject line.

Caroline Wren Press and Blair Publishing
www.blairpub.com/submissions

Literary Contest, Women, Literary Fiction, Story Collection, Novel

Carolina Wren/Blair Publishing is a small, independent press interested in publishing voices from beyond the mainstream, particularly those of underrepresented writers and authors working on subjects of cultural, natural, and historical interest in the American South and beyond.

They do not publish plays, translations, or genre fiction such as detective novels, crime novels, fantasy, or science fiction. They do not publish religious tracts, self-help books, children's books, or academic theses.

The press selects its books from the entries to three prizes: the Bakwin Award for Writing by a Female-Identifying Writer; the Lee Smith Novel Prize; and the Wren Poetry Prize. These contests typically open in the spring. Find out more by consulting their Submittable page.

www.blair.submittable.com/submit

Casagrande Press

Paul Diamond
524-L Via de la Valle
Solana Beach, CA 92075
(858) 259-0813
CasagrandePress@aol.com
www.casagrandepress.com

Nonfiction, Anthology, Creative Nonfiction, Essays, Poetry, Publishers

Casagrande Press publishes quality nonfiction, fiction, and poetry in paperback and e-book formats. Although they are a very small press and have only a few books in the catalog, Casagrande Press accepts query letters for nonfiction book projects. They often refer projects—ones that they like but cannot take on—to literary agents. Authors may query through the e-mail address above.

They also publish poetry, but their Poetry Series works like this: The author of their most recently released poetry title gets to choose the author of their next poetry title.

They do not publish fiction.

Catapult Books/Soft Skull Press
www.catapult.submittable.com/submit

Novel, Story Collection, Memoirs, Literary Magazine, Literary Fiction

Catapult publishes books of the highest literary caliber, offers writing classes taught by acclaimed emerging and established writers, produces an award-winning daily online magazine of narrative nonfiction and fiction, and hosts an open online platform where writers can showcase their own writing, find resources, and get inspired. Although their submissions' page talks about submissions for their journal, having a story accepted there may be the fastest way to get to know the editors.

Prospective authors should know that Catapult is more than a publisher. It nurtures emerging writers by helping them better their craft, and it supports more established writers by evenly sharing revenues from the classes they teach and by paying to publish their work online. Catapult strives to be a successful business model for the future of independent publishing.

This is a highly competitive publisher. Their books get reviewed in mainstream media.

CavanKerry Press

Florenz Eisman
99 Boulevard
Glen Rock, NY 07452
(201) 670-9065
www.cavankerrypress.org/submit

Poetry, Book, Creative Nonfiction, Memoir, Essays

This publisher's reading period is Feb 1-28 each year. Prospective authors must send a $20 reading fee with manuscript. They publish poetry and are looking for first authors. CavanKerry does not publish self-help, how-to, science fiction, or romance. They are partial to the writer whose distinct voice is emotionally accessible and daring. They discourage writers from sending material that is victim-ridden, pedagogic, preachy or sentimental. Works that function as soapboxes for political causes are unacceptable.

Their Laurel Books imprint publishes poetry or prose that explores in depth, the poignant and critical issues associated with confronting serious and life-threatening physical and/or psychological illness. Works that are written from a "personal" perspective, that is, by the individual who has experienced the illness will be considered. Materials written from the observer's or caretaker's view will not be considered.

Their 1st Books imprint publishes poetry or prose from writers who have never had their work published in book form. It's okay for selections from the manuscript to have been published previously in journals. A previously self-published manuscript or chapbook is not eligible for submission as a 1st Book.

Charlesbridge

Submissions Editor
85 Main Street
Watertown, MA 02472
YAsubs@charlesbridge.com
www.charlesbridge.com/pages/submissions

YA Fiction

This publisher places a premium on children's and YA books, and they are now accepting young-adult novels, which may be sent via e-mail. If sending by regular mail, mark the envelope YA NOVEL ENCLOSED.

They are open to all/most Styles, including literary and mainstream writing. They are also open to most subject matter. The editors will try to make a decision within 90 days; however, the editors do not respond to all submissions. After waiting the time indicated above, authors can assume their submission will not be accepted.

CHBB Publishing

sjdavis@chbbpublishing.com
www.chbbpublishing.com/submissions.html

New Writers, YA Fiction, Romance, YA New Adult, Novel, Fantasy

CHBB Publishing in a small, independent publisher of YA/NA paranormal romance, urban fantasy, and dystopian fiction. CHBB launched in 2012 by a consortium of authors, editors, and artists looking to give fresh and unconventional voices in fiction a chance to be heard. They accept submissions in all subgenres including contemporary, suspense, sci-fi, historical, paranormal and urban fantasy, and dystopian fiction.

Authors wishing to submit should e-mail the publisher with a brief summary of the manuscript (2 paragraphs should suffice), the word count, previous publishing credits, and any internet links to or about the author.

Authors may send the manuscript as an attachment in a Microsoft Word DOC or DOCX file, 1.5 line spacing, 12pt. font size, Times New Roman, .5 first line indents, no extra space between paragraphs, no headers/footers/page numbers, and one space between sentences, not two. Include the words "submission/name of your work" in the subject line of the e-mail.

Cider Press Review

777 Braddock Lane
Halifax, PA 17032
www.ciderpressreview.com

New Writers, Literary Contest, Literary Magazine, Poetry

CPR offers two (2) book awards each calendar year, the Editors' Prize in spring and the *Cider Press Review* Book Award in fall.

The annual *Cider Press Review* Book Award offers a $1,500 prize, publication, and 25 author's copies of a book length collection of poetry. Authors receive a standard publishing contract. The initial print run is 1,000 copies. Cider Press accepts submissions for the Book Award between September 1 and November 30 annually.

The annual *Cider Press Review* Editors' Prize offers a $1,000 prize, publication, and 25 author's copies for a book length collection of poetry. There is no first- or second-book requirement. The initial print run is not less than 1,000 copies. Cider Press accepts submissions for the Editors' Prize between April 1 and June 30 annually.

To submit to their yearly contest, send 48-80 pages of original poetry in English (individual poems may have been previously published in journals, anthologies, and chapbooks). A $26 entry fee is required. For details of formatting, see their Submittable page:

www.ciderpressreview.submittable.com/submit

Cinco Puntos

Lee Byrd
701 Texas Ave.
El Paso, TX 79901
(915) 838-1625
www.cincopuntos.com/submissions.sstg

New Writers, Hispanic, YA Fiction, Historical Fiction, New Adult, Novel

They don't always know what they're looking for until they actually see it, but the one thing that matters to them is that the writing is good, that it is work that comes from the heart and soul of the author, and that it fits well with the concerns of the press. Because *Cinco Puntos* Press focuses on the U.S. / Mexico border region, the Southwest and Mexico, they've found that many writers assume that their work will be a good fit if it likewise focuses on this area. But that isn't always true.

Before submitting a finished manuscript to *Cinco Puntos* Press, please review their existing catalog and see if the manuscript fits in with their previously published books. If that's the case, then authors are invited to call the acquisitions' editor, Lee Byrd, and speak to her directly about the manuscript before sending it. If she gives you the go ahead, send only the first 10 pages.

Although in the past they published a great many children's books, they are not currently looking for poetry or children's books.

Circling Rivers

Jean Huets
JeanH@circlingrivers.com
www.circlingrivers.com/submissions

New Writers, Nonfiction, Poetry

Circling Rivers does not publish fiction. They do not consider books, including poetry chapbooks, under 76 pages long. Note that for nonfiction they are interested primarily in works that reflect on the arts, especially literature. They're drawn to the author, known or unknown, whose work offers insight and depth, beautiful writing, and the wondrous absorption of reading.

Prospective authors may send via e-mail (to Jean Huet, above) a cover letter including:

- Word count (nonfiction) or page count (poetry) of the work;
- A succinct description of the book;
- Nonfiction queries: Provide titles of two or three published books that compare to and contrast with the manuscript;
- A paragraph about the author;
- Link to the author's website;
- And, a couple of links to previous publications, if possible.

Attached to the e-mail should be ten pages of the manuscript, preferably the first 10 pages. Send everything in the body of the e-mail. No attachments accepted. The subject line should read: QUERY: your last name, the title of your work.

City Lights Books

Editorial Dept.
261 Columbus Avenue
San Francisco, CA 94133
www.citylights.com/publishing/?fa=publishing_manuscripts

Literary Fiction, Novel, Poetry, Nonfiction, Essays

City Lights Books is an independent press that publishes twelve to sixteen titles annually in these categories: literary fiction; social, political, and cultural studies; poetry; and literature in translation.

They welcome unsolicited submissions solely in the form of book proposals, but the focus of the submission should be similar to books they've recently published. A proposal should include the following:

- A one- to two-page cover letter that describes the book and provides relevant personal and professional information
- A resume, including a list of prior publications, residencies, awards, etc.
- A sample (20 pages maximum) of the work
- With submissions of nonfiction, an outline and table of contents
- A self-addressed stamped envelope, if you wish to receive a mailed response. Proposal materials will NOT be returned. Do not bring proposals to the bookstore.

Clarity Press

Diana G. Collier
Editorial Director
2625 Piedmont Rd. NE
Suite 56
Atlanta, GA 30324
claritypress@usa.net
www.claritypress.com/ContactUs.html

Nonfiction, International

Clarity Press, Inc. is an independent publishing company that seeks to provide access to those ideas, trends and information which impact the progress of the world's peoples toward a happier, better life. Clarity titles provide an independent, objective analysis and propose solutions to some of the core issues facing us today, including issues of poverty, health care, democracy, and social justice.

Clarity publishes some of the most respected social critics of our day, coming from every shade of the political spectrum. They come from all walks of life and from diverse ethnicities and shades of the political spectrum. Some have held high positions in government or served in the United Nations; some hold credentials from or teach at prestigious universities; some have spent jail time for their beliefs.

To submit, send query letter first, with c.v., table of contents and synopsis, by e-mail to the address above. Do not send your manuscript by mail.

Coffeehouse Press

Anitra Budd
79 Thirteenth Ave NE
Suite 110
Minneapolis, MN 55413
(612) 338-0125
anitra@coffeehousepress.org
www.coffeehousepress.org

Novel, Story Collection, Memoir, Creative Nonfiction, Essays

Coffee House Press publishes emerging and midcareer authors of literary novels, full-length short story collections, poetry, creative nonfiction, book-length essays and essay collections, and the occasional memoir. Nearly all CHP authors have had works published in literary magazines or other publications (a résumé including a list of prior publications can strengthen an author's prospects). Although prior publications are important, they are not a requirement; part of the publisher's mission is to present promising debut authors alongside those who have been previously published.

The review process for full-length manuscripts can take up to 4–6 months, or longer in some instances. They only accept submissions through their Submittable portal. For notification of the next open reading period, sign up for their e-mail list.

www.coffeehousepress.submittable.com/submit

There is no fee to submit, and submissions will be capped at 300, so it is wise to send your work as early as possible.

Comma Press

ra.page@commapress.co.uk
www.commapress.co.uk

Literary Fiction, British, Anthology, Literary Magazine

Comma Press is a not-for-profit publishing initiative dedicated to promoting new writing, with an emphasis on the short story. It is committed to a spirit of risk-taking and challenging publishing, free of the commercial pressures on mainstream houses.

Comma will NOT accept whole submissions of entire collections of short stories. They will only accept single stories (or two at the most) submitted to their Dinesh Allirajah Prize fo Short Fiction, organized by the University of Lancashire and Comma Press. Each anthology has a theme, and stories must pertain to that theme.

All work must be submitted electronically by e-mail, and must include a cover letter which states the author's name, address, e-mail, contact number and story title. Without a cover letter the story will not be eligible. The submission deadline is October 25.

In addition to the anthology, Comma Press has a number of valuable resources about the writing of short stories on its website. These include video lectures on short story pioneers such as H.G. Wells, Anton Chekhov and H.P. Lovecraft.

Conari Press

65 Parker Street, Suite 7
Newburyport, MA 01950
www.redwheelweiser.com/p.php?id=8

Romance, Self-help, Nonfiction, Novel, Spirituality

Founded in Berkeley, CA in 1987, Conari Press, an imprint of Red Wheel/Weiser, publishes books on topics ranging from spirituality, personal growth, and relationships, to women's issues, parenting, and social issues. Their mission is to publish quality books that will make a difference in people's lives—how they feel about themselves and how they relate to one another. The publisher values integrity, compassion, and receptivity, both in the books they publish and in the way they do business. Their bestselling series, *Random Acts of Kindness,* is known to millions.

They welcome submissions to all of their imprints. They accept unsolicited submissions, and agented and unagented submissions. Their goal is to publish "books to live by." They adhere to no dogma, or practice, or ideology. They want to publish books that open people's eyes to looking at the world in different ways, that give them tools for improving their lives, and that inspire or instruct them.

They also have a self-publishing option through their partner company, and for that, authors will pay a fee. For more details, go here:

www.redwheelweiser.com/p.php?id=8

Copper Canyon Press

P.O. Box 271
Port Townsend, WA 98368
(877) 501-1393
www.coppercanyonpress.org/pages/engage/engage_submissions.asp

Poetry, International

Copper Canyon Press is a nonprofit publisher of poetry. They publish poets from around the world. Their open reading periods, held at least twice per year, allow them to read and consider book-length poetry manuscripts including works in translation.

They invite submissions through their Submittable portal. (They no longer read or respond to unsolicited manuscripts sent by mail or e-mail.) There is a fee of $35-$50 to submit a manuscript, depending on where the aspiring author lives in the United States or abroad. Since this is not a contest, it's possible that no manuscript will be chosen.

www.coppercanyonpress.submittable.com/submit

Cornerstone Press

University of Wisconsin-Stevens Point
325 Collins Classroom Center
1801 Fourth Ave
Stevens Point, WI 54481
cornerstone.press@uwsp.edu
www.uwsp.edu/english/cornerstone/Pages/submissions.aspx

Poetry, Essays, Story Collection, Memoirs, Novel, Creative Nonfiction

Based at the University of Wisconsin, Cornerstone Press typically focuses on up-and-coming regional authors, but they are open to all original, well-written, and polished submissions. They publish four books a year. In order to be considered for publication, manuscripts must be submitted by August 1st.

Manuscripts should be a maximum of 70,000 words. Children's book submissions, if illustrated, should include copies of artwork.

When submitting a manuscript for consideration by Cornerstone Press, include the following items:

- A one-page, single-spaced cover letter addressed to Dr. Ross K. Tangedal, Cornerstone Press. Recommended content includes a paragraph describing the manuscript you are submitting, a second paragraph describing your writing experience, and a final paragraph containing any additional information relevant to the work submitted. Within your letter, include your mailing address, e-mail address, and phone number.
- A synopsis (1-2 pages double-spaced) of the work submitted and the manuscript sent as an attachment.

Creative Nonfiction Book Award

Austin Peay State University
P.O Box 4565
Clarksville, TN 37044
www.zone3press.submittable.com/submit

Poetry, Creative Nonfiction, Literary Contest, New Writers

Zone 3 Press offers biennial book awards that alternate between poetry and creative nonfiction. The Zone 3 Press First Book Award in Poetry will open for submissions in 2020.

The prize is $1,000 and publication. The submission period is January 1-April 1. To submit, authors will be asked to send the following:

- One copy of a manuscript of 120-300 pages;
- An acknowledgments page may be included;
- $25.00 reading fee made payable to Zone 3 Press.

The reading fee includes a one-year subscription to Zone 3.

Crooked Lane

Matt Martz
submissions@crookedlanebooks.com
www.crookedlanebooks.com

Fiction, Crime, Novel, Thriller

Crooked Lane Books was founded in 2014 to publish the highest quality crime fiction titles in both print and electronic editions. From high-concept thrillers and white-knuckled suspense to traditional mysteries and literary crime, their titles consistently deliver driving plots, engaging characters, and stunning twists from the most talented authors on the scene.

Crooked Lane Books is distributed through Penguin Random House Publisher Services, giving them unparalleled access to information, new technologies, a leading supply chain, and the benefits and reach of the Penguin Random House sales force.

Crooked Lane is also represented by Biagi Literary Management for subsidiary rights licensing in foreign and domestic markets, and their business relationships include some of the most respected companies in the industry, including Bookspan, home of the country's largest book clubs, and Blackstone Audio, one of the nation's largest independent audiobook publishers.

Send your query letter, along with the first five pages of the manuscript, to the e-mail address above. Include your contact information.

Curiosity Quills Press
www.curiosityquills.com/submission-guidelines

New Writers, Fantasy, Thriller, Sci Fi, Novel, YA Fiction

At Curiosity Quills Press, the editors believe a book is a portal to another world, a break from reality that frees both mind and spirit. They want to bring a little piece of that magic to every life they touch with the written word. W. Somerset Maugham once said, "To acquire the habit of reading is to construct for yourself a refuge from almost all the miseries of life." They're looking for hard-hitting dark sci-fi, speculative fiction, and paranormal works aimed at adults, young adults, and new adults.

They provide our authors with a full-service publishing experience, marketing support, and technical know-how, and they are highly selective.

They're looking for the following:

- Thought-provoking, mind-twisting rollercoasters
- Works made with serialization in mind

Length Guidelines:

- Novellas: 15k-45k words
- Young Adult: 45k to 75k words
- New Adult / Upper YA Novels: 60k-100k words
- Adult Novels: 70k-120k words

To learn what their acquisitions editors are looking for, go here: www.curiosityquills.com/acquisitions-editors/

DAOwen Publications

www.daowenpublications.ca/submissions

Sci fi, Romance, Novel, Fiction, Children's Books

This publisher has several imprints targeting specific markets, such as horror and fantasy. While they encourage writers to submit, they do want those who submit to have the chance of being accepted for publication. Their guidelines are very straightforward.

- They only accept new, never before published works.
- When attaching the manuscript, make sure it is only the manuscript.
- Do not include cover letters or bios in your manuscript.
- A short synopsis area is provided. Use it.
- Keep the synopsis to under 200 words.
- Only submit once.
- Do not use special fonts.
- Manuscripts should be over 50,000 words.

They attempt to contact every author who submits. Understand that it can take as long as three months, depending on how many submissions they receive.

Dawn

Carol Malnor
12402 Bitney Springs Rd.
Nevada City, CA 95959
www.dawnpub.com/submission-guidelines

New Writers, Environmental, Children's Books, Creative Nonfiction

Dawn is a publishing "boutique" with a unique and limited niche. Their goal is to provide quality books for children by giving full attention to each publication. Don't send them material that:

- merely explains nature;
- is a fantasy;
- is a retelling of a legend (most legends have a strong element of the supernatural);
- is centered primarily on human foibles or classroom situations;
- is a story about animal rescue;
- is a story about pets;
- or that presents animals in an anthropomorphic light (but if something successfully enough promotes nature awareness they might bend the rule, as in *The Mouse and the Meadow*).

Dawn's "nature awareness" titles—almost always picture books—are intended to encourage an appreciation for nature and a respectful participation in it. In addition, it is increasingly important—almost mandatory—that the material be suited to supplement a school curriculum in some way.

www.dawnpub.com/submission-guidelines/

Deep Vellum Publishing

3000 Commerce St.
Dallas, TX 75226
admin@deepvellum.com
www.deepvellum.org

Translation, Novel, Literary Fiction, International

Deep Vellum is accepting submissions for future translations. At this time they are interested in contemporary international literature (high literary fiction and creative nonfiction) preferably by living authors, men and women alike, from all countries and language groups. No English language original works will be considered. No poetry, drama, or traditional nonfiction at this time (though check back as this may change).

Divertir Publishing

query@divertirpublishing.com
www.divertirpublishing.com/submission.html

Novel, Fantasy, Thriller, Sci fi, Romance, Mystery, Paranormal, Poetry

Query first. Divertir Publishing is an independent publisher located in Salem, NH. Their goal is to provide interesting and entertaining books to the world, as well as to offer new and exciting voices to readers.

Authors can refer to their "For Authors" page for more information about what they are interested in and how they compensate authors.

E-mail queries to query@divertirpublishing.com. Address the e-mail to Ken Tupper, the Publisher.

How your e-mail should look:

- Include full name in the query. Not including your full name makes it difficult to respond to the query.
- Subject: Title, genre, word count (for example: *Pride and Prune Juice*, romance, 76k)
- Body: The query letter. Queries will often be rejected based solely on the query letter, so it is important to describe the manuscript in enough detail for the publisher to determine if it would be of interest to them. Attach a synopsis and first three chapters of the manuscript in a Word DOC or RTF document.

They usually review queries within 3-6 weeks. All submissions will receive a response. If they are interested they'll request the full manuscript. If an author has not received a response in three months, feel free to inquire on the status.

Dorothy

Danielle Dutton
P.O. Box 300433
St. Louis, MO 63130
submissions@dorothyproject.com
www.dorothyproject.com/about

New Writers, Literary Fiction, Novel

Submissions should include: a brief description of the manuscript in question (no lengthy plot synopsis); a brief author's and/or translator's note, including any previous book publications; and, the first 20 pages of the manuscript pasted into the body of the e-mail. The submissions' portal typically closes on May 12 and reopens on September 1. They have published 15 books so far.

www.dorothyproject.com/books-gallery/

Recently named one of five small presses "slyly changing the industry for the better" (Flavorwire), Dorothy is dedicated to works of fiction or near fiction or about fiction, mostly by women. Each fall, they publish two new books simultaneously. They work to pair books that draw upon different aesthetic traditions, because a large part of their interest in literature lies in its possibilities, its endless stylistic and formal variety.

Dreaming Big
www.dreamingbigpublications.com/open-calls.html

Nonfiction, New Writers, Novel, Literary Fiction, Poetry, Children's books, Memoir, Audio books

Dreaming Big is a traditional small press publisher, not a vanity press and not a self-publishing service. If they decide to publish an author's work, the author would not have to pay anything. That said, they ask that authors help market and promote the book. They are not in favor of simultaneous submissions. They are not interested in hearing proposals for manuscripts that are not yet written, especially if it is fiction. They ask that authors give them the chance to thoroughly consider the manuscript before deciding to submit it elsewhere. They respond to every submission. Submit the proposal here:

www.dreamingbigpublications.com/contact-new.html

If they like the proposal, they may ask to see the manuscript. Attach a Word DOC, not a PDF or zip file, to an e-mail. To ensure the best chance for the manuscript being accepted, include the word count, genre, target audience, your name and e-mail address, and author bio inside the Word document. Not including this info is the biggest reason this publisher might reject the manuscript.

If a prospective author lives outside the United States, put that information in the proposal.

Drue Heinz Literature Prize

Eureka Bldg.
Fifth Floor
3400 Forbes Avenue
Pittsburgh, PA 15260
(412) 383-2456
www.upittpress.org/drue-heinz-literature-prize-submission-guidelines

Literary Fiction, Story Collection, Novella Literary Contest, Fiction

The University of Pittsburgh Press sponsors the Drue Heinz Literature Prize for a collection of short fiction. The prize carries a cash award of $15,000 and publication by the University of Pittsburgh Press under its standard contract.

Eligible submissions include an unpublished manuscript of short stories; two or more novellas (a novella may comprise a maximum of 130 double-spaced typed pages); or a combination of one or more novellas and short stories. Novellas are only accepted as part of a larger collection. Manuscripts may be no fewer than 150 and no more than 300 pages.

www.upress.submittable.com/submit

Stories or novellas previously published in magazines or journals or in book form as part of an anthology are eligible. It's not necessary to be a citizen of the United States to submit.

Dzanc Books

1334 Woodbourne Street
Westland, MI 48186
www.dzancbooks.submittable.com/submit

Literary Fiction, Novel, Literary Contest, New Writers, Novella

Highly competitive, Dzanc Books is looking for literary fiction that takes chances and does so with great writing. They do not mind books that do *not* fill a marketing niche. They are looking for absolutely fantastic works to fill those slots. It really is all about the writing to them.

Dzanc Books solicits submissions through three annual contests:

- the Prize for Fiction, which recognizes novels (40,000 words and up) that are daring, original, and innovative, and offers a $5,000 advance and publication;
- the Short Story Collection, which seeks well-crafted and powerful book-length collections and offers a $2,500 advance and publication;
- and a final contest which changes from year to year.

They also offer a Novella Prize that seeks sharp and creative short works between 18,000 and 40,000 words in length. The Novella Prize offers a $1,500 advance and publication.

Their contests open March 1 and close September 30. The winner of each contest, along with a short list of finalists, is announced on November 15.

EDGE Science Fiction and Fantasy Publishing

P.O. Box 1714
Calgary, Alberta
Canada T2P 2L7
(403) 254-0160
michelle@hadespublications.com
www.edgewebsite.com/submissions.html

POD, Sci fi, Fantasy

Edge is currently seeking high-quality, novel-length science fiction and fantasy. They are not interested in young adult, horror, erotica, religious fiction, short stories, dark/gruesome fantasy, or poetry. Manuscripts should be written in good taste and be aimed at an older (aged 20 and up), well-read, mature audience.

They only accept submissions of novels between 75,000 and 100,000 words. They work with new and established authors, and they use POD printing exclusively.

EDGE also occasionally publishes YA speculative fiction; however, any YA submissions must be aimed at a well-read, mature audience and be between 75,000 and 100,000 words.

For the specifics of their formatting requirements, read more here:
www.edgewebsite.com/authors.html

Elixir Press Fiction Award

P.O. Box 27029
Denver, CO 80227
www.elixirpress.com/guidelines/elixir-fiction-award

Story Collection, Novel

Elixir Press sponsors an annual fiction contest open to all writers writing in English. Both short story collections and novels are eligible. The prize is $2000, along with publication by Elixir Press and 25 copies of the book.

www.elixirpress.submittable.com/submit

To enter, authors must pay the $40 entry fee and submit between March 1-May 31.

Eludia Award

Brittany Loefler
Asst. Fiction Editor
P.O. Box 63927
Philadelphia, PA 19147
(610) 764-0813
hiddenriverarts@gmail.com
www.hiddenriverarts.wordpress.com

Novel, Story Collection, International

With a deadline of June 30, the Eludia Award is offered annually for a first, book-length, unpublished novel or collection of stories. The prize is open to women writers age 40 and older, who do not yet have a book-length publication of fiction. (Book-length publications in other genres are fine. Self-publishing is publishing, and will disqualify the fiction manuscript.)

The winning manuscript will be published on their imprint, Sowilo Press, and will receive $1000 plus a standard publication contract. The entry fee is $22 U.S. This competition is open to international submissions for all writers in English, and they encourage submissions from their international community of women writers.

All submissions must include a name, address, telephone number, e-mail, website (if an author has one one), a biography (including birthday) and resume, outline, full synopsis and full manuscript. (If submitting a collection of short stories, the "synopsis" can be a brief overview of the stories—their themes, setting, characters, etc.) Online submissions are required. Note that, when submitting online, all materials must be combined into one document before uploading. Authors should take care to upload all required materials, including the synopsis, before uploading the manuscript, which should be uploaded last. To submit online go to Submittable and submit to the category "Eludia Award".

www.hiddenriverartssubmissions.submittable.com/

If online submission is a true hardship for anyone interested in submitting to The Eludia Award, do not hesitate to contact them at hiddenriverarts@gmail.com to discuss an alternative possibility. It's not their intention to exclude anyone, but rather to simplify the reading of manuscripts. Online submissions make group evaluation possible, and it makes everything more affordable.

Be patient. Reading each manuscript at least three times—often four and five times—before naming their semi-finalists and finalists takes many months. Be sure to subscribe to their blog for all announcements. Also, and this is important, unless your manuscript on Submittable is reported as "declined", it is still in consideration.

All awards are decided by Hidden River staff, and decisions are final. All submissions will be considered for regular publication by Sowilo Press in addition to consideration for The Eludia Award.

Emily Books

submissions@emilybooks.com
www.emilybooks.com/about

Women, Memoirs, Novel, Literary Fiction

A very literary publisher, Emily Books only accepts two books a year. From 2011 to 2016, they sent subscribers a book each month via their online bookstore, selecting underappreciated novels and memoirs, mostly by women. Early in their history, they championed the work of Ellen Willis, Eileen Myles and Elena Ferrante, creating an audience of readers who trust Emily Books to send great writers their way. In 2015, they began partnering with independent publisher Coffee House Press to publish two original books a year.

They are passionate about the writing of women, trans people, and queer people, and they seek out works that challenge genre distinctions, especially the distinction between memoir and fiction.

They look for books that are funny, challenging and provocative. Their favorite writers are frank and unapologetic and make often-ignored or misunderstood subjectivities and points of view feel both relatable and utterly unique. To submit work, contact them by e-mail at the address above.

Engine Books
www.enginebooks.org/_source/home.html

New Writers, Novella, Story Collection, Literary Contest, Novel, Literary Fiction

Queries from literary agents and authors are welcome when the publisher's website indicates they're open for submissions. Include a cover letter and the first chapter (maximum 20 pages). Read their titles to become familiar with the imprint's aesthetic. Engine Books does not publish nonfiction, poetry, textbooks, or any other kind of book. Just fiction.

They're a boutique fiction press publishing novels, short story collections, collected novellas, and related volumes. They seek to publish four titles each year, ensuring full attention to the editing, production, and promotion of each title. They occasionally have a novel contest with a $2000 prize.

www.enginebooks.submittable.com/submit

ENO Publishers

P.O. Box 158
Hillsborough, NC 27278
elizabeth@enopublishers.com
www.enopublishers.org/bks/

New Writers, Nonfiction, Memoirs

ENO is a high quality, regional publisher from the Carolinas. They have many guidebooks, and they are dedicated to producing books in all formats about the culture and history of the Carolinas and the South. From the arts and the region's imaginative cuisine, to its much storied and complicated past, to the environment and the way people live in it, the South is fertile ground for publishing.

Housed in a cozy office above the LaPlace Cafe in Hillsborough, North Carolina, ENO takes its name from the river that snakes through this colonial town, and that has drawn people to settle along its banks for at least 700 years, this having been a thriving Native-American post long before Europeans arrived.

Among the many creative souls who have called Hillborough home are such celebrated writers as Lee Smith, Michael Malone, Allan Gurganus, David Payne, Craig Nova, Jill McCorkle, and Randall Kenan.

Entangled Publishing
www.entangledpublishing.com/submission-information

YA Fiction, Romance, New Adult

Entangled is an exclusive, boutique publisher of romantic fiction. Because they invest a considerable amount of time and money in every book they acquire, they are highly selective with their acquisitions. If an author has a compelling premise, a compulsively readable voice, and the drive to succeed, they'll be interested. Here are their current calls for submission.

- Amara—70k-120k word single title adult romance novels
- August—20k-70k word category romance featuring Gen-X characters
- Bliss—20k-60k sweet category romance
- Brazen—20k-60k erotic category romance
- Embrace—New Adult romance novels or novels with romantic elements
- Entangled Teen—70k-120k word romance novels or novels with romantic elements
- Indulgence—45k-60k contemporary category romance
- Lovestruck—20k-60k contemporary, romantic comedy category romance
- Scandalous—20k-65k historical category romance
- Scorched—15k-65k novellas, serialized novellas, and full-length novels, all with erotic romance elements
- Teen Crave—20k-60k paranormal/scifi/fantasy YA category romance
- Teen Crush—20k-60k contemporary YA category romance

eTreasures Publishing
www.etreasurespublishing.com

Romance, Sci fi, Mystery, Fantasy

This is a Christian publisher open to a broad range of adults, children, and young adults. Here are the genres they're currently publishing:

- Action-Adventure
- Fantasy
- Historical
- Paranormal.
- Horror
- Mystery/Crime
- Romance
- Science Fiction
- Suspense/Thriller

They use POD publishing for all of their paperbacks.

Etruscan Press

84 South Street
Wilkes-Barre, PA 18766
etruscanpress@gmail.com
www.etruscanpress.org/community-resources/submissions

New Writers, Story Collection, Literary Fiction, Essays, Memoirs, Novel, Creative Nonfiction

The publisher considers manuscripts year round, but submissiOns must be accompanied by a $20 reading fee.

www.etruscanpress.submittable.com/submit

Founded in 2001 with a generous grant from the Oristaglio Foundation, Etruscan Press is a non-profit cooperative of poets and writers working to produce and promote books that nurture the dialogue among genres, achieve a distinctive voice, and reshape the literary and cultural histories of which they are a part.

They publish books of poems, novels, short stories, creative nonfiction, criticism, and anthologies. Two of their poetry collections have been National Book Award finalists. Etruscan is proud of support received from the National Endowment for the Arts, Ohio Arts Council, and the Nathalie and James Andrews Foundation, as well as many private contributors.

Currently housed in the creative writing program of Wilkes University, Etruscan is distributed nationally by Small Press Distribution and Bookmasters, which means that an author has a small chance of getting into bookstores.

Evolved Publishing
www.evolvedpub.com/submissions

Crime, Romance, Horror, Mystery, Thriller, New Writers, Fantasy, Novel

Evolved describes itself as a hybrid small press. They refer to their authors, editors, and artists as team members because they function in an enthusiastic, cooperative, information-sharing, team environment. That's a matter of organizational management style—they operate in such a way as to make the experience a positive, creative, supportive one for all their teammates. It keeps morale high, and everyone focused on the tasks-at-hand—writing and selling quality books.

Evolved primarily focuses its efforts on the emerging market of e-books, but they also produce audiobooks and print books via POD (Print-on-Demand) through Lightning Source (Ingram), and they tackle all genres and sub-genres, so long as the work meets their tough standards. Their mantra, practically their religion, is simple: Quality is Priority #1.

Authors are not required to pay up-front fees to publish with them. They do offer that option for services such as editing or cover art, in case the author wishes to maximize their royalty rate (can be as high as 81% of retailer royalties paid), but that is entirely up to the author. They offer more options, not fewer, and give the author greater control to determine the best course of action for his or her own career. Their author royalty rates are among the highest (perhaps the highest) in the industry.

Falstaff Books

www.falstaffbooks.com/submissions

Story Collection, Novel, Westerns, Romance, Fiction, Fantasy

Falstaff Books is a digital and print publishing company based in Charlotte, NC and dedicated to bringing to life the best in fantasy, science fiction, horror, mystery, and dramatic literature. The battered, ignored, rejected "misfit toys" of fiction are all welcome at Falstaff Books, where they understand that every scar is a story and only with different voices can harmony be created. Their next call for *submissions will be in 2021.* Here's what they're looking for:

- Fantasy
- Horror
- Mystery/Crime
- Science Fiction
- Westerns and weird Westerns

FC2

P.O. Box 303
Buffalo, NY 14201-0303
www.fc2.org/prizes.html

Story Collection, Novella, Literary Contest, New Writers, Novel

As publishers of independent, innovative fiction, FC2 selects its book from two contests: the Sukenick and Doctorow contests. They're open to short story collections, one or more novellas, or novels, and there are no length requirements.

For the Sukenick contest ($1500 plus publication by University of Alabama Press), an author doesn't need previous publications. For the Doctorow contest, an author needs three previous books. The winner of each contest will receive a $15,000 prize and publication by the University of Alabama Press. Use Submittable to submit, and submit during their reading period, August 15 to November 1.

www.fictioncollective2.submittable.com/Submit

Featherproof Books
Jason Sommer, Editor
submissions@featherproof.com
www.featherproof.com/about-us

Novella, Poetry

Featherproof Books is a young, indie publisher based in Chicago, and they're dedicated to the small-press ideals of finding fresh, urban voices. They publish perfect-bound, full-length works of fiction and downloadable mini-books. Their novels are filled with the liveliest of fiction wrapped in the loveliest of designs. Their mini-books are carefully designed short stories and novellas that may be downloaded from their website, printed and constructed by the reader, inviting all ten fingers to take part in the book-making process. They view all of their authors as creative partners, which means the author is involved in every step of publication, and always expected to buy the next round.

Felony & Mayhem Press

174 W 4th St.
Suite 261
New York, NY 10014
submissions@felonyandmayhempress.com
www.felonyandmayhem.com/committing-your-own-mayhem

Historical Fiction, Novel, Literary Fiction

What they claim to be looking for is "the best in intelligent, literary mystery fiction." Felony & Mayhem Press is open to all/most subgenres, excluding hardboiled. Many of their books have historical settings.

They ask that authors send the following and only the following:

- a brief synopsis;
- and, a representative chapter, which may, but need not be the first chapter.

In writing the synopsis, authors should confine themselves to a maximum of four short paragraphs. The purpose here is to offer a rough outline of the story, not to give a scene-by-scene breakdown, as in a shooting-script. When they go into the movie business, they'll let you know.

Books should be 80,000 words with 85,000 preferred. Send the materials outlined on the submissions' page above to their e-mail address.

Fernwood Publishing (Canadian)
roseway@fernpub.ca
www.fernwoodpublishing.ca/submissions

Journalism, International, Canadian, Nonfiction, Essays, Novel, Literary Fiction

Historically, Fernwood Publishing has published primarily for an academic audience. To this end, they publish books intended for undergraduate university and college courses and monographs intended as supplementary texts in all levels of undergraduate and graduate courses. Their main focus is in the social sciences, with an emphasis on criminology, aboriginal studies, labour studies, women's studies, gender studies, critical theory, politics, political economy, cultural studies and social work.

Roseway Publishing is an imprint of Fernwood Publishing and publishes literary works related to social injustices and the struggles involved in making the world a better place. They publish works of fiction, creative nonfiction, biographies and other literary writing that is in keeping with their interest in social justice issues.

Roseway Publishing is primarily interested in publishing for an adult audience but publishes young adult material as well. They tend not to publish children's literature or poetry.

Filter Press

P.O. Box 95
Palmer Lake, CO 80133
(888) 570-2663
www.filterpressbooks.com

Novel, YA Fiction, Nonfiction, Historical Fiction, YA, New Adult

This is a publisher with a focus on Colorado and the Southwest. They have a limited number of authors, and authors wishing to submit have the best chance if they can write about the history of the region.

For nonfiction book proposals, they will consider and advise if the work looks appropriate, but they make no publishing commitments until a book is complete.

Submit in hardcopy (not on computer disk or by e-mail) to their address above. Authors who wish manuscripts returned must provide a self-addressed, stamped envelope.

www.filterpressbooks.com/about.html#AboutUsSubs

The press often has a backlog of manuscripts to evaluate, so it can be several months before they give you a decision on publication.

After contracting with the author to publish, Filter Press needs at least six months for editing, layout and design, and printing. Since they publish only four to six titles each year, and normally have several in progress, the elapsed time for seeing the book in print may be 12-18 months.

Flannery O'Connor Award for Short Fiction

Erika Stevens
University of Georgia Press
330 Research Drive
Athens, GA 30602-4901
www.ugapress.org/index.php/series/FOC

Story Collection, Literary Fiction, Literary Contest

More than seventy short-story collections have appeared in the Flannery O'Connor Award series, which was established to encourage gifted emerging writers by bringing their work to a national readership. The first prize-winning book was published in 1983; the award has since become an important proving ground for writers and a showcase for the talent and promise that have brought about a resurgence in the short story as a genre.

Winners are selected through an annual competition that attracts as many as three hundred manuscripts, many written by authors who have graduated from MFA programs in Creative Writing. This is one of the most prestigious literary awards in the U.S.

Submissions are open from April 1 to May 31 each year. Winners of the Flannery O'Connor Award for Short Fiction include such widely read authors as Ha Jin, Antonya Nelson, Rita Ciresi, and Mary Hood.

www.georgiapress.submittable.com/submit

Fleur-de-Lis Press

c/o The Louisville Review
Spalding University
851 South Fourth Street
Louisville KY 40203
www2.spalding.edu/louisvillereview/press.html

New Writers, Story Collection, Poetry, Literary Magazine, Literary Fiction

The primary mission of the Fleur-de-Lis Press is to publish first books of authors who have appeared in *The Louisville Review*, a literary magazine. The press currently has fourteen such books in print.

www.louisvillereview.org/submissions/

Other books by Fleur-de-Lis are *High Horse: Contemporary Writing* by the MFA Faculty of Spalding University; *Place Gives Rise to Spirit: Writers on Louisville*, a book of essays and photographs about Louisville, and *You Are Not Here* by David Jauss, the winner of the 2002 Fleur-de-Lis Poetry Contest.

The best way to get their attention is to submit to the literary magazine, *The Louisville Review*.

Floris Books' Kelpies Prize

15 Harrison Gardens
Edinburgh, Scotland
United Kingdom EH11 1SH
floris@florisbooks.co.uk
www.discoverkelpies.co.uk/kelpies-prizes

Children's Books, Literary Contest, Fiction, Scottish, Novel

Writers and illustrators based in Scotland are invited to win a year of mentoring with an experienced editorial and design team, a publishing contract, a £1,000 cash prize, and more.

Winners of both the writing and illustration contests will also be invited to spend a week-long writing retreat at Moniack Mhor or join a high-powered conference for book illustrators, Picture Hooks.

For full details see the appropriate links below:

www.discoverkelpies.co.uk/kelpies-prizes/kelpies-prize-writing/enter/

www.discoverkelpies.co.uk/kelpies-prizes/kelpies-prize-illustration/enter/

Fomite Press

Marc Estrin

www.fomitepress.com/FOMITE/Submissions.html

New Writers, Poetry, Essays, Creative Nonfiction, Literary Fiction, Nonfiction, Novel, Story Collection

This small, Vermont press is so overwhelmed at the moment with long submissions and second and third drafts that they have had to call a temporary halt to reading new material. Check back later. If the green light is on the home page, they're open for submissions.

At this point, the editor Marc Estrin is the only one requesting, receiving or reading manuscripts. Consequently, acceptance comes down to "what Marc likes." When submissions reopen, and if you want Fomite to consider a manuscript, authors should e-mail the editor a description of the work, the opening section, and the author's favorite writing in the book.

Fomite gets little or nothing beyond expenses. They have no plans to "make money" with the press, only to serve the writing community by bringing out high-level literary work and making it available. Fomite uses print on demand (POD) and e-book technology to publish novels, short story collections, poetry and selected nonfiction works.

Founders House Publishing

614 Wayne Street, Suite 200A
Danville, IL 61832
submissions@foundershousepublishing.com
www.foundershousepublishing.com/p/submissions_14.html

New Writers, Sci fi, Fantasy, Novella, Novel, Steampunk

Although Founders House Publishing's submissions are currently closed, when they reopen, they will be looking for Science Fiction and Fantasy. In particular, they are looking for books in the following subcategories: sword & sorcery, space opera, paranormal (including paranormal romance), deindustrial SciFi, superhero-themed, dark fantasy (bordering on horror), urban fantasy, steampunk, and alternative history.

They want books that are between the following lengths: 30,000 to 50,000 words. This word count range includes novellas and shorter novels. They will announce when their focus is changing or if they expand word counts.

They say that their royalty payments are generous. When they reopen, include a cover letter in the body of the e-mail, a two-paragraph summary of the book, and the complete manuscript as an attachment.

Send a paper manuscript in the traditional Shunn format:
www.shunn.net/format/novel.html
All submissions may be sent to:
submissions@foundershousepublishing.com.

Four Way Books

P.O. Box 535
Village Station
New York, NY 10014
(212) 334-5430
editors@fourwaybooks.com
www.fourwaybooks.com

Literary Magazine, Story Collection, Novella, Poetry

For a book-length collection of poetry written in English, Four Way Books offers the Levis Prize in Poetry. It's open to any poet writing in English, regardless of publication history. The winner will receive a $1000.00 honorarium and participation in a Four Way Books' reading in NYC.

During their June 1-30 open reading period, authors may submit book-length poetry collections, story collections and novellas. They do not publish novels, translations, or nonfiction. They will respond by mid-November.

They also offer the "It's No Contest" contest for a book-length collection of poetry in English by a New York City resident (5 boroughs) emerging writer for a first or second collection of poems. The reading period is November 15-December 15.

Authors should mail their manuscript in one Microsoft Word DOC or PDF file and include all contact information. Include acknowledgments, biography, and a table of contents. The book should not be fewer than 45 pages of text. The manuscript should be sent through their submissions manager:

www.fourwayreview.com/submissions/

Fugue State Press

P.O. Box 80
Cooper Station
New York, NY 10276
www.fuguestatepress.com/guide.html

Novel, Literary Fiction

This publisher is looking for innovative novels. They aren't looking for poetry, short stories, or nonfiction books. Only send them novels. They're looking for experimental novels that are ambitious, visionary, private, idiosyncratic, emotional. They often enjoy prose that's broken and writing in which the flaws are obvious and grow out of emotional necessity.

Genre work is not what they publish. Don't send thrillers, detective novels, children's books, fantasy, or science fiction.

They're very arbitrary in their likes and dislikes, and often turn down genuinely brilliant work—sometimes a lot better work than they've published—just because it doesn't seem right. It's all down to the odd tastes of the editor. (Also realize that they get about a thousand book submissions a year, and publish only three in a good year.)

Query first, using the form below.
www.fuguestatepress.com/submissions.html

Gival Press

Robert Giron
Gival Press, LLC
P.O. Box 3812
Arlington, VA 22203
givalpress@yahoo.com
www.givalpress.submittable.com/submit

Hispanic, Literary Contest, New Writers, Poetry, Novel

Gival Press, LLC, an award-winning independent literary publishing house located in Arlington, Virginia, publishes fiction, nonfiction (essays and educational texts), and poetry. To promote writing, Gival Press sponsors four annual contests for fiction and poetry. Their publications are in English, French, and Spanish.

They publish the work of authors (poets / writers) from many walks of life who demonstrate quality and whose work has a message, be it philosophical or social.

Their literary contests award cash prizes for which a reading fee is required.

- Gival Press Novel Award, deadline May 30th
- Gival Press Oscar Wilde Award, deadline June 27th
- Gival Press Short Story Award, deadline August 8th
- Gival Press Poetry Award, deadline December 15th

Golden Fleece Press
www.goldenfleecepress.com/submissions/

YA Fiction, Anthology, Novella, Children's Books, Novel, Memoirs

Golden Fleece is a full service publisher committed to publishing diverse, original works in any genre. They accept short stories, poetry, and artwork for their multiple compilation projects, as well as full length novels, novellas, memoirs, and nonfiction manuscripts. They are charity-focused, with a portion of net proceeds from most projects donated to charity.

Check their submissions' guidelines on the link above.

Goldline Press Chapbook Competition

editors@goldlinepress.com
www.goldlinepress.com

Literary Contest, Poetry, Chapbook

Goldline Press, a publishing arm of USC's Dana and David Dornsife College of Letters, Arts, and Sciences, publishes chapbooks and poetry.

Manuscripts must be 20-30 pages in length for poetry entries, and 7,500-15,000 words for fiction and nonfiction entries (not including the title page and table of contents). Submit the manuscript typed in a font such as Times New Roman or Arial. Alternative fonts such as Didot are difficult to read on a digital screen.

Manuscripts should be paginated with a table of contents at the beginning, unless the form of the book does not warrant it. Include a cover page with title of manuscript only. No identifying material should appear anywhere in the body of the manuscript. Your identifying information will be available to them via their submission manager when needed.

Do not include an acknowledgments page. Individual poems/short stories/essays may have been previously published, but the work as a whole must be unpublished.

The manuscript must be in English. Translations are ineligible. The $15 entry fee ($18 for applicants outside the U.S. or Canada) includes a copy of the winning chapbook in your genre.

All manuscripts must be received between July 15 and August 31 via Submittable:

www.goldlinepress.submittable.com/submit

Gordian Knot Books

Jane Altschuler
Richard Altschuler & Associates, Inc.
100 West 57th Street
Suite 2M
New York, NY 10019
Jaltschuler@rcn.com
www.richardaltschuler.com/html/gkb.html

Nonfiction, Creative Nonfiction, Essays

The mission of Gordian Knot Books is to publish quality nonfiction anthologies and monographs that give readers the information and insight they need to understand and formulate solutions to social, legal, medical, and technical-scientific problems. A great deal of their focus is on medicine and psychology.

Guernica Editions

425 Adelaide St. W.
Suite 700
Toronto, ON
Canada M5V 3C1
michaelmirolla@guernicaeditions.com
www.guernicaeditions.com/contact

Children's Books, Canadian, Memoirs, International, Essays, Creative Nonfiction, Story Collection, Novel, Literary Fiction, Genre fiction

This is a high quality literary press based in Canada, and they *do* accept non-agented submissions. As with their queries, they will only accept manuscripts via e-mail attachment. Send manuscripts as Word documents (DOC or RTF) to michaelmirolla@guernicaeditions.com. The manuscripts should be single-spaced, in a 12-point, easy-to-read type. If at all possible, give the manuscripts a name that includes the title and the author, such as The_Dubliners_Franz_Kafka.

While they do their best to respond ASAP to queries and requested manuscripts, note that it may take from six to eight months before an evaluation can be made and a response generated.

Guernica's annual reading period runs from January 1 to April 30. Submissions are only accepted during this period and only as e-mail attachments.

Aside from the original Guernica Editions imprint (pertaining to literary and cultural material), they have expanded the publishing house to include a MiroLand imprint. Under MiroLand, they accept queries in the areas of memoir, how-to, self-help, graphic novels, art books, cookbooks and children's literature, as well as genre literature. When querying for the MiroLand imprint, indicate as much.

Gypsy Shadow Publishing
www.gypsyshadow.com/Guidelines.html

New Writers, Fairy Tales, Fantasy, Novella, Historical Fiction, Novel, Sci fi, Thriller, Nonfiction

Gypsy Shadow publishes high-quality well-written manuscripts in a variety of genres and lengths. They want novelettes, short story collections, novellas, novels, and nonfiction work. They publish first novels if they are of professional quality.

They accept manuscripts of 10,000 to 50,000+ words in length. Any manuscript longer than 50,000 words contracted for publication will be placed in the queue for publication at the earliest possible date. As prospective authors will see on the www.gypsyshadow.com homepage, they have a variety of original genres.

- Fireflies includes books which are fantasies and modern fairytales.
- Moonbeams are the science fiction, time travel and alternate reality books.
- Riddles are mysteries, suspense, horror, enigma and adventure stories.
- Shadow Dance includes dark fantasy, paranormal and supernatural stories.
- Dusky Moon includes erotica and hot romance (extremely limited).
- Bard's World is poetry, songs and lyrics (no longer accepted for publication).
- The Grove includes nonfiction except history.
- The Guild is for books about arts and crafts.
- Legends are tales of history, folklore, alternate history, historical fiction and religious fiction.
- New Springs is their youth and young adult section.
- Stardust stories are mainstream romances and chick lit.
- The Wee Folk section is for children's stories.
- March Winds is the free reads and sample chapters section, if you would like to submit works to be included as an example of your writing style.

Hanging Loose Press

231 Wyckoff St.
Brooklyn, NY 11217
print225@gmail.com
www.hangingloosepress.com/submissions.html

Literary Fiction, Literary Magazine, Poetry

The best way to have a book published by them is to send something to their magazine. Since 1966, they have published 107 issues of *Hanging Loose* magazine and 240 books, mostly poetry. They published first books by Sherman Alexie, Kimiko Hahn, D. Nurkse, Joanna Fuhrman, and Maggie Nelson, among others, plus titles by Harvey Shapiro, Ha Jin, Elizabeth Swados, Jayne Cortez, Paul Violi, Charles North, Tony Towle, Joan Larkin, and many more. The emphasis is on innovative, energetic work, with a stress on new writers and neglected older writers.

Head of Zeus
www.headofzeus.com/about-us

Fiction, Historical Fiction, British, Mystery, Literary Fiction

Head of Zeus is an award-winning, independent publisher of genre fiction, narrative nonfiction and children's books. They are based in Clerkenwell, London, but their reach is global. Over the last seven years, they have published 93 (and counting) #1 bestsellers around the world and won 14 literary prizes and two industry awards. All their writers, whether debut authors or *Sunday Times'* bestsellers, are published in digital, print and audio formats with a zeal that merges talent with tradecraft and technology.

Prospective authors must subscribe to their newsletter before submitting, and prospective authors can only submit when the publisher opens submissions. This is a British publisher.

Go here for the specifics of how to submit:

www.headofzeus.com/articles/8a452134-6d00-4250-9e84-7a2f686f5440

Heliotrope Books
heliotropebooks@gmail.com
www.heliotropebooks.com/submissions/

New Writers, Memoirs, Contemporary fiction, Nonfiction, Novel, Creative Nonfiction

This publisher is a commercial/literary press with an open reading period from Sept. 1-Oct. 15. Books compete not only with each other (over 300,000 books are published annually in the United States alone) but also with television, sports, streaming and social media. Since they're competing heavily for a reader's time, this publisher offers books that intrigue and entertain, teach and mentor—and challenge the reader's mind. They're also looking for books that can be used in educational curricula or be adapted for film or television.

Since they're a small press, they accept few titles each year. They seek authors who understand how to reach their audience and market their books "out of the box." Each book is its own small business that deserves a customized marketing plan. They're looking for authors who understand that the book will not "make" them—but rather, that they have the power to "make" the book.

They accept agented submissions as well as unagented submissions, and prefer a personal recommendation or introduction. Acquisitions are made bi-annually, on May 1 and November 1.

Authors interested in working with them should submit the first 20-30 pages of a manuscript, an outline, author bio, and marketing plan between September 1 and October 15, for the November 1 acquisition deadline. Submit to heliotropebooks@gmail.com with the word "Submission" in the subject line.

Henery Press
www.henerypress.com/about

New Writers, Mystery, Novel

This publisher is looking for mysteries (all genres) and chick lit in the 65K-90k word range. They like cozy mysteries and prefer mysteries with a splash of chick lit. They focus on the cozier side of life: cozies with a hook, cozies with an edge, cozies with humor, and cozies with adventure.

They're fortunate to have had five books hit the *USA Today* bestseller list, and multiple books that have won industry awards and garnered nominations (Agatha, Macavity, Daphne, Golden Heart). All books are available in e-books, trade paperbacks, and hardcovers. They pay royalties to their authors while offering editorial guidance, engaging cover artwork, and a structured, turn-key social media strategy.

Heydey Into California

www.heydaybooks.com/submission-guidelines

Nonfiction, Memoirs, Environmental, Novel, Creative Nonfiction

This publisher is regional to California. Heyday is an independent, nonprofit publisher and unique cultural institution. They promote widespread awareness and celebration of California's many cultures, landscapes, and boundary-breaking ideas. Through their well-crafted books, public events, and innovative outreach programs, they are building a vibrant community of readers, writers, and thinkers.

They publish books on cultural and natural history, especially native history, and California art and literature. Their reading period opens and closes, depending on the number of manuscripts they have under consideration, so check their website for current requirements.

Hobblebush Books

17-A Old Milford Road
Brookline, NH 03033
(603) 672-4317
hobblebush@charter.net
www.hobblebush.com/submissions

Custom Books, Fiction, Poetry

Authors wishing to have a manuscript considered must have a New Hampshire connection. They do have a design service that can provide an "assisted publishing" solution for authors who want to self-publish, but don't have the design skills.

They publish only a small number of titles each year, and therefore do not accept unsolicited manuscripts. If an author has a book that seems like a good fit for Hobblebush, send them a query by e-mail or mail, including biographical information and prior publishing history.

They publish poetry only in the Hobblebush Granite State Poetry Series, and this is only for New Hampshire authors or authors with a very strong New Hampshire connection.

They publish fiction only in the Hobblebush Granite State Short Story Series, and this is only for New Hampshire authors or authors with a very strong New Hampshire connection.

An author interested in paid services, using their own imprint, should visit the Hobblebush Design page.

House of Anansi Press

110 Spadina Ave.
Suite 801
Toronto, ON
Canada M5V 2K4
www.site.houseofanansi.com/anansi-submissions

Poetry, Nonfiction, Novel, Canadian, Creative Nonfiction

Anansi publishes Canadian and international writers of literary fiction, poetry, and serious nonfiction. They publish approximately twenty new books a year, four of which are poetry. They have a roster of talented authors who have previously published with them and continue to produce award-winning, progressive new works.

Anansi publishes literary fiction that has a unique flair, memorable characters, and a strong narrative voice. Anansi fiction writers have read widely, studied their craft, and often have previously published in reputable literary journals and/or magazines. They typically publish five titles a year.

Anansi's nonfiction titles are meticulously researched to support a strong thesis. They avoid dry, jargon-filled academic prose and have a literary twist that will interest general readers and experts alike.

Anansi publishes poets who have already established a strong reputation. Anansi poets usually have had poems previously published in book form or in reputable literary journals and/or magazines.

Anansi does not accept unsolicited materials from non-Canadian writers. Canadian writers should read their submissions' requirements for details.

Howling Bird Press

110 Spadina Avenue
Suite 801
Toronto, ON
Canada M5V 2K4
www.site.houseofanansi.com/anansi-submissions

Poetry, Nonfiction, Novel, Canadian, Creative Nonfiction, Literary Contest

Howling Bird Press is open for submissions of creative nonfiction manuscripts: memoir, personal essays, literary journalism, food writing, travel writing, and more. Word counts should be in the 20,000 to 50,000 range. File formats should be either a Microsoft DOC or DOCX. Pages should be numbered, and the author's name and address should appear on the first page. Simultaneous and multiple submissions are allowed.

Howling Bird Press is the publishing house of Augsburg University's MFA in Creative Writing. Their book prize alternates genres annually, from poetry to fiction to nonfiction. Previous winners include Marci Vogel, Jacob M. Appel, Jean Harper, and Kate Lynn Hibbard.

Include a cover letter in the form provided online, and list contact information and a short (100 to 200 word) bio. There is a $25 entry fee. The deadline is July 31. The winner is announced in January and receives $1,000 and book publication the following fall.

Howling Bird Press books are distributed by Small Press Distribution and are available online and at fine bookstores nationwide.

Hub City Press
www.hubcity.org/press/submissions

Creative Nonfiction, Story Collection, New Writers, Literary Contest, Novel, Literary Fiction

Hub City Press publishes books of literary fiction, creative nonfiction, regional nonfiction, nature, and art. Hub City is a small press, publishing five to eight titles per year. In general, their publication schedule operates at least 12-18 months in advance of release.

Authors should send a one-page query letter. Submissions are open in March to April and September through October. Check their Submittable page to see what they are currently looking for.

www.hubcity.submittable.com/submit

Their preference is to communicate by e-mail, so authors should include an e-mail address in the query letter. They *do not* accept submissions in the following categories: romance, science fiction, true crime, mystery, cookbooks, how-to books, horror/paranormal or specific-religion inspirational books.

Do not send them a query for books that have already been self-published, even only as e-books.

International Book Publishers Association

1020 Manhattan Beach Blvd.
Suite 204
Manhattan Beach, CA 90266
(310) 546-1818
info@IBPA-online.org
www.ibpa-online.org

Book

The IBPA is a large, vibrant community of independent publishers, self-published authors, and vendors providing services to the book industry.

The organization is a good place to look for additional independent publishers not listed in this book. But, it's also a rich source of information about building a financially self-sustaining author career. They offer substantial discounts on identifiers and bar codes, design and editorial services, admission to book fairs, shipping services, and sales and distribution vendors. All in all, they have a wealth of information for anyone wanting to get a sense of the publishing industry. You do not have to be a member to search their vendors, but once inside the door, you will discover a wealth of material to guide you on your author journey.

IF SF

ifsfpublishing@gmail.com
www.ifsfpublishing.com/submissions

Novel, Nonfiction, Literary Fiction, Memoirs, Creative Nonfiction

IF SF is now reading manuscripts and project proposals for future publication. They've expanded their catalog to include creative nonfiction, memoir, the arts, and the great outdoors with a special emphasis on the West. Any serious submission by artists who are familiar with their publishing history and who feel a compatibility with their editorial goals will be considered.

Founded in 1999 in Los Angeles as If Publications and now located in San Francisco, IF SF is a not-for-profit press that has published books in a range of genres, including memoir, poetry, and photography. IF SF's books are now in the archives of both private and institutional collectors in the U.S. and abroad.

The IF SF imprint, praised in the past for publishing the work of "voices that deserve to be heard" in books of visually arresting formats, is known for taking a collaborative approach to each project, inviting the artist to take part in the creation of the book. Each IF SF book is published in the medium best suited to the material.

While continuing to focus on the literary and graphic arts, IF SF remains open to the projects of interest in other categories.

Ig Publishing

Robert Lasner
P.O. Box 2547
New York, NY 10163
(718) 797-0676
robert@igpub.com
www.igpub.com/about-ig

Story Collection, Nonfiction, Literary Fiction, Novel

Ig publishes original literary fiction from writers who have been overlooked by the mainstream publishing establishment and political and cultural nonfiction with a progressive bent. They are open to a broad audience, including: adults, middle grades, young adults, and all sexual identities.

Ig does not accept unsolicited manuscripts, either by e-mail or regular mail. Authors wishing to have a manuscript considered must send a query to the attention of Robert Lasner, Editor-in-Chief. If they are interested, they will contact you. All unsolicited manuscripts sent to them via e-mail or regular mail will be discarded. They prefer to receive queries via e-mail only.

Impress Books
www.impress-books.co.uk/impress-prize

New Writers, Mystery, Crime, British, Historical Fiction, Novel, Literary Contest

The Impress Books prize was created to discover and publish new writing talent in fiction and nonfiction. Entries are selected by the editors and a panel of publishing professionals.

The winner of the prize is offered a publishing contract with Impress Books. The Impress team also looks at all entries, with a view to publication. Numerous entries from previous years have gone on to be published by Impress Books and other publishers, and many authors who have entered the prize have also gone on to be represented by agents. The prize closes to submissions on 30th June at 5pm GMT, the shortlist will be announced on 21st August, and the winner will be announced at the end of September.

It is their firm belief that the prize is not just about the winner but should encourage emerging authors. To find out more about the prize, follow them on Twitter using @ImpressPrize and @ImpressBooks1.

Impress Books was founded in 2004 as an independent publishing house focusing on previously unpublished writers of nonfiction and fiction. Their list now specializes in historical fiction, crime, and contemporary fiction. In 2015, Impress launched a new digital-first imprint called Watchword, which is dedicated to publishing the new and more experimental forms of fiction. Impress continues to introduce new writers into the publishing industry with the Impress Prize for New Writers, a competition designed exclusively for writers who have not previously been traditionally published. Details can be found on the website above.

Ink Smith Publishing
www.ink-smith.com/submissions

New Writers, Thriller, Sci fi, Mystery, Fantasy, Novel

This publisher specializes in publishing several genres as well as developing a close relationship with their authors. It is their goal to be the best independent publisher for new to fully established authors. Submissions will be accepted January 1 -July 30 each year, with a closed reading period beginning August 1.

Aspiring authors should query first. They have a limited demographic. Submissions are restricted to people in the U.S. or Canada. They want to publish books for those who believe in their story.

An author who has a game plan for marketing and a vision for where they want to go is a huge plus. Knowledge of social media sites like Facebook and Twitter is also important.

Interlink Publishing

46 Crosby Street
Northampton, MA 01060
www.interlinkbooks.com/pages.php?page=submission

New Writers, Nonfiction, International

Authors are advised to become familiar with the kinds of books they publish. If, after doing this research, an author believes the manuscript might fit their list, send a query letter via e-mail with the appropriate subject heading.

The query letter should include: a writing sample (preferably the opening of the book) of no more than 10 pages, a brief synopsis, and biographical information about the author and, when appropriate, translator. The query letter should be included in the body of the e-mail, and the writing sample should be attached as a Microsoft Word PDF, RTF, or DOC file.

Send the e-mail with the subject heading "QUERY" followed by the genre and title of the manuscript, e.g., your cookbook manuscript titled *The Middle Eastern Kitchen* would be sent with the subject "QUERY: Cookbook: The Middle Eastern Kitchen."

All nonfiction queries, including cookbooks and travel, as well as general inquiries, should go to submissions@interlinkbooks.com. Fiction submissions should be sent to fiction@interlinkbooks.com.

Iowa Prize in Literary Nonfiction

University of Iowa Press
119 West Park Road
100 Kuhl House
Iowa City, IA 52242-1000
www.uipress.uiowa.edu/authors/iowa-nonfiction.htm

New Writers, Nonfiction, Creative Nonfiction, Literary Contest

The Iowa Prize in Literary Nonfiction, open to both new and established writers, is awarded for a book-length manuscript of literary nonfiction originally written in English.

Collections that include previously published periodical articles are eligible as long as the author has retained copyright. Work that has been previously self-published in its entirety is not eligible.

Manuscripts should be at least 40,000 words long, but may not exceed 90,000 words. Manuscripts should be doubled-spaced. The author's name should appear on the title page only. Submit a hard copy of the manuscript. E-mail entries will not be accepted. Manuscripts will be recycled. Do not include return packaging or postage.

Submissions must be postmarked on or between October 15, and December 10. No exceptions. A $10 administrative fee is payable to the University of Iowa Press. They consider simultaneous submissions, but ask that authors notify the press immediately if the manuscript should be accepted elsewhere. Only the winners will be notified.

Iowa Short Fiction Award

Iowa Writers' Workshop
507 North Clinton Street
102 Dey House
Iowa City, IA 52242-1000
www.uiowapress.org/search/browse-series/browse-JSSF.htm

New Writers, Literary Fiction, Story Collection, Literary Contest, International

Any writer who has not previously published a volume of prose fiction is eligible to enter the competition. Previously entered manuscripts that have been revised may be resubmitted. Writers are still eligible if they have published a volume of poetry or any work in a language other than English or if they have self-published a work in a small print run. Writers are still eligible if they are living abroad or are non-U.S. citizens writing in English.

The manuscript must be a collection of short stories in English of at least 150 word-processed, double-spaced pages. They do not accept e-mail submissions. The manuscript may include a cover page and contents page, but these are not required. The author's name can be on every page, but this is not required. Stories previously published in periodicals are eligible for inclusion.

There is no reading fee. Do not send cash, checks, or money orders. Reasonable care is taken, but they are not responsible for manuscripts lost in the mail or for the return of those not accompanied by a self-addressed, stamped envelope. The submission must be postmarked between August 1 and September 30. They assume the author retains a copy of the manuscript.

Island Press

www.islandpress.org/submit-proposal

Nonfiction, Environmental

With more than 800 titles in print, Island Press is a leading provider of environmental solutions and information. Their publishing program develops, publishes, markets, and distributes original, empowering books in conjunction with other environmental organizations, academic institutions, and government agencies. Each editorial decision they make is based on extensive market research that reveals an unmet need in such areas as ecosystem management, land-use planning and sustainable communities, and environmental policy.

Island Press editorial staff interacts regularly with the education and environmental community—scientists, environmentalists, professionals, public officials, community leaders, instructors, students, and concerned citizens—to assess what information they need to better carry out their efforts to protect the environment. Their editors also attend academic, scientific, and professional association conferences and formally survey Island Press book buyers for market research. They use the feedback to develop the content and format of their books and to continually refine the various elements of their overall publishing program, from the composition of the annual new title list to the design of their marketing strategies. To have your work considered, follow their instructions on submitting a proposal.

Jai-Alai Books
www.jai-alaibooks.com

Story Collection, Novel, Nonfiction, New Writers, Memoirs, Literary Fiction

Jai-Alai Books publishes literary titles in all genres, and they are based in Dade County, FL. They make books for Miami, meaning that they're interested in books that arise from Miami-Dade County's unique cultural landscape and/or books that will speak to Miami-Dade County readers.

Jai-Alai only publishes around three titles a year. They're a small, independent press with independent distribution. Jai-Alai is a labor of love. Everyone who works for this publisher volunteers his or her time. They are rarely able to provide advances or royalties. They put more time, energy, and care into each book than the vast majority of publishers.

They accept proposals in all genres: fiction, nonfiction, poetry, memoir, comics, graphic novel, hybrid, etc. Use Submittable to send a cover letter with a brief biographical statement. They will need a 150-word summary of the book (or book idea), a sample chapter or section, and a $4.99 reading fee.

www.omiami.submittable.com/submit

Jolly Fish Press

www.jollyfishpress.com/submissions.html

Fantasy, Romance, Sci fi, YA Fiction

This publisher produces high-quality middle-grade and YA fiction, especially books showcasing strong voices, unique stories, and diverse characters. They're always looking for science fiction and fantasy with an epic and visual scope; thrillers with strong, carefully crafted characters and a unique voice; and unconventional love stories.

Before submitting a manuscript, make sure it is finished, completely proofread, and edited. The submission should include a one-page query; one-page synopsis (spoilers included); and, the first three chapters.

Queries should adhere to these basic outlines:

- Paragraph One—The Hook
- Paragraph Two—Mini-Synopsis
- Paragraph Three—Writer's Bio

JournalStone Publishing

www.journalstone.com

YA Fiction, Fantasy, Horror, Sci fi

JournalStone publishes fantasy, horror, and sci fi. Submissions are free. They do not charge any fees to authors. If they approve a submission for publication, they will make the investment in the author and his or her book.

Simultaneous submissions are okay, but let them know that the work has been sent out to other markets, and notify them if it gets accepted elsewhere. If the book has been previously published, they will not consider it. They read from June 1-July 31. Go here to read details of their requirements.

www.journalstone.com/journalstone-submissions/

Juniper Prize for Fiction

Mary Dougherty
University of Massachusetts Press
East Experiment Station
671 N. Pleasant Street
Amherst, MA 01003
potts@umpress.umass.edu
www.umass.edu/umpress/contact/juniper-prize-fiction

Story Collection, Novella, Literary Contest, Novel

The Juniper Prize for Fiction is awarded annually to two original manuscripts of fiction: one short fiction collection and one novel. The University of Massachusetts Press publishes the winning manuscripts and the authors receive a $1,000 award upon publication.

Submissions will only be accepted between August 1 and September 30 yearly. The entry fee is $30, and all manuscripts will be judged anonymously by a distinguished writer of fiction from the UMass Amherst MFA program. The award winner will be announced on their website in April, with publication slated for the following Spring.

The competition is open to all writers in English, whether or not they are U.S. citizens.

Novels and collections of stories are all eligible. Work that has previously appeared in magazines, in whole or in part, may be included, but should be so identified on the cover sheet. Manuscripts must be at least 150 pages and no longer than 350 pages.

www.umasspress.submittable.com

Katherine Anne Porter Prize

English Department
University of Texas at Arlington
203 Carlisle Hall
P.O. Box 19035
Arlington, TX 76019
www.untpress.unt.edu/for-potential-authors

Literary Contest, Novella

The University of North Texas Press publishes books via the Katherine Anne Porter Prize in Short Fiction. The winner of this annual award will receive $1000 and publication by UNT Press. Entries will be judged by an eminent writer.

Manuscripts may be submitted between May 1 and June 30. The winning manuscript will be announced in January.

Entries can be a combination of short-shorts, short stories, and novellas, from 100 to 200 book pages in length (word count between 27,500 and 50,000). Material should be previously unpublished in book form. Once a winner is declared and contracted for publication, UNT Press will hold the rights to the stories in the winning collection. They may no longer be under consideration for serial publication elsewhere and must be withdrawn by the author from consideration. The $25 entry fee can be paid online via credit card or PayPal.

Stories included in the submission may have appeared previously in magazines or anthologies but may not have been previously published in a book-length collection of the author's own work.

www.universityofnorthtexaspress.submittable.com/submit

Kattywompus Press
www.kattywompuspress.com

Poetry, Memoirs, Chapbook

This press only publishes chapbooks, meaning anything that wants to live on about 30 text pages or less. There is no genre restriction. For full length manuscripts, they will consider the first 20 pages. If they like that excerpt, they'll ask an author to send the full manuscript.

They also do limited editions, special bindings, unique artist's books, musical-literary publications, and other wackadoodle projects. Query with brief description. *Poets Greatest Hits* is invitation-only by the selection panel.

All submissions must be sent via e-mail as a Microsoft Word DOC attachment. Generally, chapbook manuscripts should be 20 to 36 pages of text with one poem per page.

They put a lot of time, energy and love into reviewing submissions. They make no promises of editorial feedback, but they often include it with both acceptance and rejection letters. They ask in return that authors invest a $15 reading fee to have their work considered. Query them with any questions:

contact@kattywompuspress.com.

Kent State University Press

Will Underwood
1118 Library
1125 Risman Drive
P.O. Box 5190
Kent, OH 44242-0001
(330) 672-7913
wunderwo@kent.edu
www.kentstateuniversitypress.com/category/series/lit_med

Novel, Nonfiction, Memoirs, Literary Fiction

The Kent State University Press welcomes inquiries and proposals in their fields of publication, listed below. Prospective authors should send a letter or e-mail of inquiry briefly describing the project to Acquiring Editor, Will Underwood, following which an author may be invited to submit a proposal.

Proposals should be sent digitally via e-mail. The Press does not return unsolicited materials or accept unsolicited manuscripts. Fiction and memoirs about human health are being considered now. They are also interested in the following subjects:

- Ohio and the surrounding region
- Sports
- U.S. history, especially the Civil War era and abolitionism
- Military
- True crime
- Hemingway
- C.S. Lewis, J.R.R. Tolkien, and the Inklings

They do not publish fiction, except occasionally within their Literature & Medicine series.

Kitaab Publishing House
www.kitaab.org/publishing

New Writers, Story Collection, Novel

This publisher has an international focus and aspires to connect Asian writers with readers globally. They are open to all styles, including literary.

Knopf

The Editors
1745 Broadway
New York, NY 10019
www.knopfdoubleday.com/contact-us

Novel, Fiction, Literary Fiction

Knopf usually only accepts manuscripts submitted by an agent. They recommend that authors consult *The Writer's Market*, available in a local bookstore, from an online retailer, or a library. The website at www.writersdigest.com is also a good source of information.

If an author still wants to give them a try, though, even with that caveat, send a sample of 25-50 pages and a stamped, self-addressed envelope to the address above. It will be reviewed with other unsolicited work. Allow approximately 12 months for a response. Also be aware that they are unable to accept manuscripts submitted via e-mail.

Larson Publications

Paul Cash
4936 NYS Route 414
Burdett, NY 14818
paul@larsonpublications.com
www.larsonpublications.com/submission-guidelines.php

Self-help, Memoirs

What they want most isn't out there yet. They hope they'll recognize it when they see it. Authors can improve their chances by being as clear about the subject matter as possible.

Of the many issues that threaten our mutual well-being on this earth together, which does the book address? What is the author saying about it that hasn't been said, or said well, or already ignored?

Send a query letter, with an enclosed stamped, self-addressed envelope, to the address above. Allow at least eight weeks for them to respond. Don't be surprised if they take longer. They don't accept e-mail queries, but they ask you for an e-mail address to respond with questions, ask for a full proposal or sample chapters, or the whole manuscript.

Lavender Ink

www.lavenderink.org/content/about

Hispanic, Poetry, New Writers, Story Collection, Novel, Literary Fiction, International

Lavender Ink and *Diálogos* welcome submissions via their Submission Manager. They are interested in any work of literary merit in any genre, including anthologies or collections, but their main interest is in the broad categories of contemporary poetry, fiction, and literature in translation.

While their two imprints represent different categories of publications, authors need not concern themselves with which imprint you are submitting to. The two imprints emphasize the following:

- Lavender Ink: Contemporary Poetry, Fiction and other genres in English.
- *Diálogos*: Works of international or cross-cultural significance, including works in translation and/or any work which engages multiple cultures. Such work will often have a political component.

To submit a manuscript, upload the complete manuscript, prefaced by a letter of introduction and biographical note listing publications and any other relevant data, all in a single document. If the work is a translation or anthology, include information about publication rights.

They do not pay advances, but they do pay royalties. A standard royalty arrangement would be 30% of net proceeds. Note that royalties are calculated on the net, not on the list price. Authors are expected to do their own promotion.

www.dialogos.submittable.com/submit

LCk Publishing

P.O. Box 628
Stevenson, WA 98648
www.lckpublishing.com/submission

Story Collection, Novella, Novel, Literary Fiction

They're looking for novels or novellas and short story/essay collections.

Manuscripts must be double-spaced and include a synopsis. For short story collections, send three to five stories that best represent the project. Poems do not have to be double-spaced. Send five to ten poems. A poetry collection must have at least forty poems for consideration. All files must be submitted in PDF format or in a Word document. Submit manuscripts in the form provided on the above page.

Allow 4 to 6 weeks for an official response.

Leapfrog Press

Luke Daly

www.leapfrogpress.com/submissions.htm

YA Fiction, Novella, Story Collection, Novel, Sci fi, Literary Fiction

All fiction submissions will only be accepted through their annual fiction contest, which will be open from January 15 through May 1. (See their contest page later in the year for details).

Adult, young adult (YA) and middle grade (MG) novels, novellas, and short story collections are accepted. Minimum word count: 22,000. Individual stories in a collection may have been published in journals. Books that have been self-published will be considered "unpublished" if fewer than 200 copies were printed.

They are interested in publishing literary fiction and mainstream fiction, including science fiction. Generally they are less interested in strict genre fiction, but if a manuscript is good and grabs their attention, they dom't care what the genre is.

They accept queries and contest submissions only through their Submittable page. Their needs are very special. They are looking for that rare book that combines dark and light, satire and honesty, emotional range and pure joy of invention. They like books on the edge of avant garde. They are particularly interested in works that are quirky, that fall outside of any known genre, and of course are well written and finely crafted. Although they have a small number of popular fiction titles, their focus is literary fiction. They publish mainly adult fiction, and only occasionally take nonfiction.

Legend Press

submissions@legend-paperbooks.co.uk
www.legendtimesgroup.co.uk/legend-press/submissions

Mystery, Historical Fiction, British, Sci fi

Legend Press has a commitment to quality and originality. Their list varies from commercial crime to quirky cult titles as well as historical. Each book is precious, and they pride themselves on working closely with their authors to get the most out of every book.

They have a highly selective list so that they can provide the editorial support and promotional activities necessary for an author's success. They focus on publishing fiction, so unfortunately they do not accept anything outside of this, including children's books, poetry or travel writing. They can only consider complete manuscripts. Read through their recent catalogues and familiarize yourself with the types of books they've previously published.

They receive a huge number of submissions, and therefore ask authors to be patient. They aim to respond within 4-6 months and cannot offer individual feedback. For all queries regarding submissions, visit their FAQs page or get in touch via the e-mail address above.

Literary Wanderlust
www.literarywanderlust.com/submissions/

Nonfiction, Westerns, Novel, Historical Fiction, Romance, Sci fi, Crime, Mystery, Fantasy

At Literary Wanderlust they strive to publish well-written fiction. They are a small, traditional publisher located in Denver, Colorado. They are currently accepting: Women's fiction and Romance, Science Fiction and Fantasy, Mystery and Thriller, Historical Fiction, and Nonfiction.

They do not accept self-published or previously published books, nor are they interested in novellas, picture books, chapter books, short stories, or nonfiction.

Livingston Press

University of West Alabama
Station 22
Livingston, AL 35470
jwt@uwa.edu
www.livingstonpress.uwa.edu/htm%20(web%20pages)/tartt_first_fiction_award.htm

Story Collection, New Writers, Literary Contest

Livingston Press was founded in 1983 by Charles Henley as a means to publish regional authors. Under Joe Musso in 1988, the press expanded. Again, in 1993, the press expanded its focus to publish "offbeat & Southern literature," as well as regional history. They now have authors from Seattle, New York City, Boulder, and Tampa. The press publishes ten titles a year, and its books are distributed nationally.

Although they are currently closed to novel submissions, they are still running their Tartts Fiction Award, which publishes short story collections. The author can have published a novel, but not a collection of stories. They gravitate toward "offbeat and Southern" stories. By "offbeat," they mean stylistically, mostly—either in the form or the author's language. Their next Tartts Story Collection Contest closes on December 31.

Of their past dozen books, many have been reviewed in national newspapers or magazines, and several have been reviewed in either *Publishers Weekly, New York Times Book Review, Booklist, Library Journal,* or *Kirkus Reviews.* A few have been reviewed in two or more of these.

Lookout Books

Department of Creative Writing
University of North Carolina Wilmington
601 S. College Road
Wilmington, NC 28403
www.lookout.org

Story Collection, Novel, Literary Fiction

Lookout Books, a nonprofit affiliated with a university, produces one or two books of high literary merit each year. They no longer read unsolicited submissions by authors with no representation. The best way to introduce your work to them is by submitting to their partner magazine *Ecotone*. They invite book submissions from the pool of *Ecotone* contributors.

www.ecotonemagazine.org/submissions/

Ecotone is open to submissions via Submittable above, from August 15–October 1, and from December 15–February 1. There is a $3 fee to use the online system. On completion of your submission, they'll send you a discount for $3 off a year's subscription (or renewal) to the magazine.

Loose Leaves Publishing

Megan Eichenlaub
5158 S Lavender Moon Way
Tucson, AZ 85746
info@looseleavespublishing.com
www.looseleavespublishing.com

Poetry, New Writers, Literary Fiction, Historical Fiction, Women's Fiction, Magical Realism

Loose Leaves is an independent publisher of quality fiction and nonfiction books, founded in 2012 and based in Tucson, Arizona. They are professionals who love books and choose only the finest manuscripts for publishing. They build relationships with both new and established writers by selecting works based on their own judgment rather than a corporate policy. They are personally invested in both the author and the author's work.

The editors work closely with authors to reach their intended audience. Following the author's plan, they assist with submissions for literary prizes and critical review. They support book signings, book giveaways, and produce press releases, bookmarks, and other promotional materials.

Send a Microsoft Word DOC, Pages, or RTF document to the e-mail address above. Include all items specified in the Submission Checklist. If they like what they see, they will request the entire book.

Love Knot Books

www.loveknotbooks.ca/manuscript-submission-2/submission-guidelines

New Writers, Novel, Romance

Romance only. When submitting, do not use more than 200 words to describe your manuscript. While they may accept work under 50,000 words, they will not publish anything under 30,000 words unless a second story is added to increase the word count. They publish both digital, print, and audio. Their publisher meets new authors over Skype to discuss the publication process.

They attempt to contact every author who submits to them. Please understand that it can take as long as three months depending on how many submissions they receive.

Once accepted, a manuscript goes through three editing steps:

- Structural / Content
- Stylistic / Line
- Spelling / Grammar / Punctuation

Great care is taken during the editing stages to remain true to the author's overriding style. Keep in mind the work must adhere to proper spelling and grammar to be publishable.

They do not accept previously published work. Only submit once. Do not use special fonts.

LSU Press

Rand Dotson
3990 West Lakeshore Drive
Baton Rouge, LA 70808
www.lsupress.org/submissions#Submitting

Story Collection, Literary Fiction, Novel, Poetry, Nonfiction

LSU Press publishes two fiction titles per year. Fiction proposals should include a cover letter, a one-page summary of the work, a brief sample from the work, and a current resume. Poetry proposals should include a cover letter, 4–5 sample pages from the manuscript, and a current resume. They do not accept e-mailed queries for fiction.

In short, give as much information as is useful to help them evaluate your proposal, but do not send the entire manuscript. Initially the manuscript will be considered in-house. If they agree that the work has potential for their list, they will notify you and send the manuscript to outside anonymous readers for review. The review process normally takes four to six months. All positively reviewed manuscripts must be approved by the University Press Committee before the editors can proceed toward publication. For specific information about their acquisition editors, visit their website.

Mad Creek Books

Kristen Elias Rowley
Editor-in-Chief
180 Pressey Hall
1070 Carmack Road
Columbus, OH 43210-1002
thejournalmag@gmail.com
www.ohiostatepress.org/authors/prospectiveauthors.html

Story Collection, Literary Fiction, Novella, Novel, Creative Nonfiction, Latino, Comics, Poetry

Mad Creek Books is a new literary trade imprint from The Ohio State University Press. With a mission to foster creativity, innovate, and illuminate, Mad Creek Books champions diverse and creative literary writing. A platform for artistic, daring, and innovative literary books—also, in nonfiction, fiction, and poetry—books on the Mad Creek imprint push boundaries, explore new areas, and generate new ideas. Mad Creek Books is a place for exciting literary work and will publish writers from all experiences and backgrounds, representing the true diversity of the literary landscape.

New book series on the imprint include Machete, 21st Century Essays, Latinographix, and The Journal Non/Fiction and Poetry annual prize series. They will also publish books outside of these series. Contact Kristen Elias Rowley, Editor-in-Chief, for queries about the imprint, series, or to submit a manuscript or proposal.

Main Street Rag

P.O. Box 690100
Charlotte, NC 28227-7001
(704) 573-2516
editor@mainstreetrag.com
www.mainstreetrag.com

Poetry, Anthology Novella, Novel, Literary Fiction, Literary Magazine

Main Street Rag publishes 90 titles per year and specializes in print runs of 50 or more. Avoid reading fees by subscribing to their literary magazine.

Main Street Rag Publishing Company is an independent publisher of poetry, fiction, and creative nonfiction as well as a print, bindery, and production house for other publishers. They own the equipment on which their books are produced. As a production house, they print and bind books for other publishers, but that does not mean they will do anything that someone else is paying them to do. Top on that list is "Print-On-Demand" projects. Although they have some equipment in common with POD, it is not their method of choice, and they are not interested in projects with print runs of less than 50 copies.

Their magazine, *Main Street Rag*, is strictly for poetry. The editors select manuscripts through contests, through recommendations from authors they've published, and through the submission options listed below. On average they publish between 60 and 90 poetry collections every year. It is the genre for which they are best known.

Their partner imprint, Mint Hill Books, is open for submissions from May 1-June 15. This is where to submit anthologies, creative nonfiction, memoirs, novellas, novels, and short fiction collections. Their yearly target is as many as a dozen works of prose per year.

No simultaneous submissions. Submit by going here:
www.mainstreetmag.submittable.com/submit

McSweeney's Books

www.mcsweeneys.net/pages/guidelines-for-book-submissions

Novel, Nonfiction

This publisher is very selective. That only accept electronic manuscripts through their submissions' portal.

They are often closed to submissions, but when submissions reopen on Submittable, authors will see that there are no length requirements. Because they are a very small organization with an even smaller editorial department, it often takes a long time to respond to submitters. For the moment, they do not publish children's books or poetry.

Perhaps the best way to gain an inroad with these folks is to submit to their print or online magazine. This is a good market for wry humor.

www.mcsweeneysbooksubmissions.submittable.com/submit

Meerkat Press
www.meerkatpress.com/submissions

YA Fiction, Mystery, Romance, YA New Adult, Novel, Literary Fiction, Thriller, Mystery, Speculative Fiction

The editors are looking for original stories that make their brains engage, breaths catch and hearts thud. They love fresh voices, unique/flawed characters, imaginative story lines, and diversity in characters and settings (and authors!) Their catalog does have a high percentage of speculative fiction and darker themes, but that's not all they publish, so please feel free to submit work that you think fits their needs.

If an author has a completed work that falls into one of the categories above, they will consider it. Manuscripts must be between 40,000 and 100k. Include a cover e-mail containing genre, word count, pitch, brief bio, and contact information. Please confirm that your story has not been published before (self-published is considered previously published), and send a full synopsis of up to 3 pages.

For specific details of formatting and submission procedures, see their website and upload a Microsoft Word DOC, DOCX, or RTF file here: Submissions@MeerkatPress.com.

Royalties, marketing plan and budget, editorial process, and expectations will be thoroughly discussed prior to signing. They only publish books they love, so if accepted, an author will have a publisher/champion/partner working with them every step of the way!

They try to be as quick with their responses, but they are a small press and aren't always reading submissions. That is why simultaneous submissions are not only accepted, but also encouraged (as long as you notify them promptly if your work is accepted elsewhere).

Melange Books

www.melange-books.com

Women's Fiction, Romance, Erotica, YA, New Adult

Melange is open for submissions in the categories above.
This is a royalty-paying company that publishes e-books (digital formats) and print books. They pay authors 40% net royalties on digital formats and 20% on print. They are actively seeking submissions.

www.melange-books.com/subs.html

- Authors wishing to send a Young Adult and New Adult submission are advised to visit Fire and Ice YA Books

www.fireandiceya.com/

- For Romance submissions, visit their brand new Satin Romance website for submission guidelines.

www.satinromance.com

Melange seeks to satisfy every reader's taste in romance literature. Read specific instructions for manuscript formatting and send submissions to the Publisher, Nancy Schumacher:

submissions-nancy@melange-books.com

Mercer University Press
Editor-in-Chief
1501 Mercer University Drive
Macon, GA 31207
www.mupress.org/Assets/ClientPages/Submission-Guidelines.aspx

YA Fiction, Women's Fiction, Mystery, Romance, New Writers, Novel

Mercer University Press, affiliated with the Baptist Church, seeks to publish scholarly works of excellence in the following fields:

- Religious Studies, particularly Biblical Studies;
- Philosophy;
- Southern Culture, particularly History of the South;
- and, Fiction/Literary.

As a university press, MUP strives for accuracy of substance and form. Works will be considered that represent only the highest standards of scholarly research and literary style. The publication process for unsolicited works begins when a prospective author sends a book proposal to the Editor-in-Chief.

Miami University Press Novella Prize

Dana Leonard
356 Bachelor Hall
Miami University
Oxford, OH 45056
(513) 529-2602
mupress@muohio.edu
www.orgs.miamioh.edu/mupress/novella/index.html

Novella, Literary Contest, New Writers

The Miami University Novella Prize is awarded annually to a novella-length manuscript of original fiction (18,000–40,000 words). The winner receives $750, a standard contract, publication, and 10 copies of the book.

The submission deadline is always October 15. All entrants must pay a reading fee of $25. The length must be 18,000-40,000 words. Unfortunately, shorter or longer manuscripts will be disqualified without refund.

Format Requirements: Manuscripts should be double-spaced, using a standard 12 pt. font, and should include page numbers. Be sure your name does not appear anywhere on the manuscript. Previously published works are not eligible. Simultaneous submissions are welcomed. All entries and fee payment must be sent through Submittable.

www.mupress.submittable.com/submit

Michigan State University Press

1405 South Harrison Rd.
Suite 25
East Lansing, MI 48823
msupress.org/books/submissions

Nonfiction, Creative Nonfiction, Poetry

Initial submissions to MSU Press should be in the form of a short letter of inquiry and a sample chapter, as well as their Acquisitions' Questionnaire. Download their Acquisitions' Questionnaire from their website, fill it out, and mail it with the manuscript. Their fiction must be Michigan related and is by invitation only.

They do not accept:

- Unsolicited works of fiction, memoir, or poetry.
- Simultaneous manuscript submissions.

Michigan University Press

The University of Michigan Press
839 Greene Street
Ann Arbor, MI 48104-3209
ump.fiction@umich.edu
www.press.umich.edu/series.do?id=UM141

Story Collection, Literary Fiction, Novel

In addition to their annual Michigan Literary Fiction Awards (see the weblink above), MUP also publishes literary fiction linked to the Great Lakes region. Such fiction is part of their Sweetwater Fiction series. They welcome both new and established authors. They have no restrictions as to style or subject matter, but are unlikely to consider genre fiction, such as mystery, religious, science fiction, romance, and children's fiction.

To ensure that your work receives proper attention, they ask that you submit (via regular mail) a cover letter and a sample consisting of approximately the first thirty pages (or two stories) of the manuscript. Provided that your work meets the above requirements, there is no need to query in advance. Work submitted without an SASE will not receive a response.

Send materials to the MUP Fiction Editor at the address above. Due to USPS safety regulations requiring that packages over 16 oz. be hand delivered directly to a post office worker, they are unable to return manuscripts, even with an SASE. Do not send your only copy of the work.

Milkweed Editions

Open Book Building
Suite 300
1011 Washington Ave. South
Minneapolis, MN 55415-1246
(612) 332-3192
webmaster@milkweed.org
www.milkweed.org/submissions

Poetry, Story Collection, Literary Fiction, Creative Nonfiction, Novel, Novella, Nonfiction

Highly selective, Milkweed Editions publishes literary fiction, nonfiction about the natural world, poetry, and novels for young readers. Works of fiction (novels, novellas, and short story collections) are between 150 and 400 pages. They do not publish genre fiction, by which they mean they are not interested in romance, science fiction, mystery, crime, or westerns.

Milkweed is looking for manuscripts of high literary quality that embody humane values and contribute to cultural understanding, and to that end, they offer a National Fiction Prize. Milkweed has restructured the prize: in the past they have solicited manuscripts specifically for the contest, but for all future contests, Milkweed Editions will award the National Fiction Prize to the best work of fiction Milkweed accepts for publication during each calendar year by a writer not previously published by Milkweed Editions.

Submission directly to the contest is no longer necessary. Since they will now be choosing the winner from the manuscripts accepted for publication during a given year, all manuscripts submitted to Milkweed will automatically be considered for the prize. Judging will be by Milkweed Editions' editors, and the winner of the prize will receive a $5,000 cash advance as part of any royalties agreed upon in the contractual arrangement negotiated at the time of acceptance.

Please see the website for reading periods and submit your manuscript during the appropriate reading window.

Montag Press

www.montagpress.com/submit

Fantasy, Horror, Novel, Sci fi, Anthology

Montag Press is primarily a publisher of fiction anthologies. They offer a 70/30 share with the author for worldwide primary and secondary rights including digital, options, film and video production, and print rights, which will be exclusive for 10 years from the date of publication.

Typical calls for submission include such themes as the following: 1) a juried short story anthology tentatively titled "Hardboiled" exploring the intersection of changing roles of masculinity, the manosphere, male rights, dis/empowerment, technology, gender norms and expectations, and male sexuality; 2) an anthology tentatively titled "The Track : Streetwalkers" exploring the culture, economy and power politics of street prostitution, streetwalkers, prostitutes, whores, pimps, johns, mongers, cops and community members. The stories should be titled with the name of the protagonist. These are examples only. Check the website for their current needs.

In general, they are not looking for private investigator stories, covert action stories, undercover cop stories, male chick-lit romances, or war stories, unless the traditional genre conventions are examined and possibly inverted.

Negative Capability

Sue Brannan Walker
62 Ridgelawn Drive East
Mobile, AL 36608
(251) 591-2922
swalker@negativecapabilitypress.org
www.negativecapabilitypress.org/submissions

Literary Fiction, Novel, Poetry

This is an extremely selective literary press affiliated with *Negative Capability*, a literary magazine. The press publishes one or two books of fiction a year. Their main focus is on poetry, and the easiest way to gain the attention of the editors is to submit poetry via the Eve of St. Agnes Poetry Competition.

The Eve of St. Agnes is the designated eve when Agnes would go to bed without supper, undress, and dream of her husband to be. Poems may be any form–but no more than 250 lines.

Up to 10 poems may be submitted for $5.00 per poem. Former judges include Ann Deagon, X.J. Kennedy, Margaret Atwood, W.D. Snodgrass (who took one of the finalists to dinner when he was traveling through Louisiana), Marge Piercy (who waived her judges' fee to add an additional award), Marvin Bell, Leo Connellan, Michael Bugeja, and James Dickey (who wrote the finalists, commented on their poems, and suggested places to publish in addition to *Negative Capability*).

New Issues Press

Western Michigan University
www.wmich.edu/newissues

Literary Contest, Poetry

Submit poetry only during the open reading period for their annual poetry prize. The prize includes $1,000, publication, and a paid reading at Western Michigan University for a book of poems by an established poet.

The contest is open to poets writing in English who have already published one or more full-length collections of poetry. The editors will consider individual collections and volumes of new and selected poems. Besides the winner, New Issues Press may publish as many as three additional manuscripts from this competition.

Include a $30 reading fee along with the manuscript. Checks should be made payable to New Issues Press. The annual postmark deadline is September 30. The winning manuscript will be named the following January. Do not send your only copy of the manuscript.

New Libri Press
query@newlibri.com
www.newlibri.com/submissions

Story Collection, Novel

Literary, mainstream, and quirky, this micro press likes fiction with a humorous or ironic bent. It's okay to submit story collections, but don't send them romance.

New Pulp Press

editor@newpulppress.com
www.newpulppress.com/submissionrequirements.html

Crime, New Writers, Novel

New Pulp Press is a virtual publisher of the best in edgy crime fiction, neo-noir and neo-pulp in both e-book format (downloadable for most major eReader devices) and trade paperback format. They're looking for manuscripts 50,000 to 85,000 words in length.

New Rivers Press

151 Glenwood Street
Manchester, CT 06040
www.newriverspress.submishmash.com/Submit

Sci fi, Anthology, Literary Contest, Literary Magazine, Story Collection

New Rivers Press selects its books from entries submitted during its annual American Fiction contests with full details on Submishmash.

The contest reading period is Feb. 1 to May 1, and there is a $12 reading fee. There are three cash prizes awarded:

- First Prize: $1,000
- Second Prize: $500
- Third Prize: $250

New Star Books

Rolf Maurer
3477 Commercial St.
Suite 107
Vancouver, BC
Canada V5N 4E8
(604) 738-9429
info@newstarbooks.com
www.newstarbooks.com/contact.php

Novel, Nonfiction, Literary Fiction, Canadian

New Star is a regional Canadian publisher that accepts and reads unsolicited manuscripts. If you "get" what they do and have a proposal that you think will fit into their list, consider them. Their focus is on:

- Social issues and politics
- The culture and history of British Columbia and the West

They're looking for literary prose, both fiction and nonfiction.

They also publish poetry, although they do not consider unsolicited poetry manuscripts.

Proposals for the New Star list should be sent directly to New Star's editorial offices in Vancouver, either by mail or e-mail.

New Vessel Press
www.newvesselpress.com/

Journalism, Nonfiction, Translation, Novel, Literary Fiction, International

New Vessel Press publishes work in translation, not original books. If you would like to propose a fiction or nonfiction work, submit *only* through the Submittable portal:

www.newvesselpress.submittable.com/submit

New Vessel Press, founded in New York City in 2012, is an independent publishing house specializing in the translation of foreign literature into English. Their books are available in quality paperback and e-book formats.

By bringing readers foreign literature and narrative nonfiction, they offer captivating, thought-provoking works with beautifully-designed covers and high production values. They scour the globe looking for the best stories, knowing that only about three percent of the books published in the United States each year are translations. That leaves a lot of great literature still to be discovered.

At New Vessel Press, they believe that knowledge of foreign cultures and literatures enriches readers' lives by offering passageways to understand and embrace the world. They also regard literary translation as both craft and art, enabling them to traverse borders and open minds. They are committed to books that offer erudition and enjoyment, that stimulate and scintillate, that transform and transport.

And of course, what matters most is not where the authors hail from, or what language they write in. The most important thing is the quality of the work itself. And hence their name. They publish great books, just in a new vessel.

Their books have received a wide array of accolades, from *The New York Times* and *The Wall Street Journal* to *The New Yorker* and *O, The Oprah Magazine.* They look forward to bringing the world's great literature to ever more readers.

New Victoria Publishers

P.O. Box 13173
Chicago, IL 60613
NewVictoriaPub@att.net
www.newvictoria.com

LGBQ, Mystery, Memoirs, New Writers, Novel, Travel Narratives, Sci fi, Romance

This publisher is primarily looking for well-crafted fiction in all genres featuring lesbian protagonists with a strong sense of self-awareness.

The following ingredients should be present:

- A clear narrative story line with distinctive voice and style;
- Well drawn, intelligent, introspective characters interacting in dynamic scenes;
- Accurate background locations and atmosphere;
- Issues pertinent to the lesbian community whether emotional, societal, or political;
- And, humor and/or eroticism. Eroticism must have a feminist and consensual sensibility.

They are especially interested in lesbian or feminist manuscripts, ideally with characters who can evolve through a series of books. Mysteries should have a complex plot, and accurate legal and police procedural detail, and protagonists must have full emotional lives. Romance and adventure stories can certainly be competitive in today's market when there is a good pace, style and tension, and when the characters contain or dramatize important issues.

They also consider well-researched nonfiction of interest to womyn, as well as lesbian-feminist herstory, or biography of interest to a general as well as an academic audience.

In any science/speculative fiction or fantasy, they prefer Amazon adventure themes and/or detailed, well-crafted alternative realities, complete with appropriately original language and culture.

They advise you to look through their catalog or visit their website to see their past editorial decisions as well as what they are currently marketing. Their books average 80-100,000 words, or 200-220 single-spaced pages.

No electronic queries will be considered. send your query to them via U.S. Mail with:

- a brief bio of yourself, including all your contact information;
- a brief outline or synopsis highlighting key issues in the story, why you wrote it, and any target audience you have in mind;
- and, several sample chapters or approximately 50 pages, double-spaced.

A stamped, self addressed envelope is required if you wish to have your submission returned. Let them know if you have submitted your manuscript to other publishers.

NeWest Press

109 St.
Suite 8540
Suite 201
Edmonton, AB
Canada T6G 1E6
(780) 432-9427
www.newestpress.com/submissions

Canadian, Mystery, Novel, Literary Fiction, Plays

Founded in 1977, NeWest Press is one of Canada's first independent literary publishing houses. NeWest publishes literary fiction, literary nonfiction, poetry, and drama, as well as a line of mystery novels.

NeWest is seeking outstanding literary works by established and emerging Canadian authors. On average, they publish from 10 to 12 books a year. Their list includes fiction (including mysteries), poetry, drama, and nonfiction works with literary merit; they are especially interested in publishing books by Western Canadian authors and Western Canadian themes.

Notable NeWest titles include *Blood Relations and Other Plays* by Sharon Pollock, *Chorus of Mushrooms* by Hiromi Goto, *Icefields* by Thomas Wharton, *Diamond Grill* by Fred Wah, *Playing Dead* by Rudy Wiebe, *The Widows* by Suzette Mayr, *All of Baba's Children* by Myrna Kostash, *The Bone Cage* by Angie Abdou, *Extensions* by Myrna Dey, *Dance, Gladys, Dance* by Cassie Stocks, and *The Shore Girl* by Fran Kimmel.

NewSouth Books

www.newsouthbooks.com/pages/submission-guidelines

YA Fiction, Nonfiction, Novel, Children's Books

NewSouth publishes regional books of national interest, and they do consider unagented work, but occasionally close submissions to get caught up.

In general, NewSouth Books publishes quality works of nonfiction, fiction, and poetry, with a special interest in regional history, biography, autobiography, nonfiction, folklore, African-American, Native-American, and civil rights subjects.

The main NewSouth imprint publishes quality illustrated and non-illustrated works of fiction and nonfiction for young readers. They are especially interested in biographies of African-Americans and in concise, interesting books that make understandable to young readers such complex subjects as slavery, segregation, the Civil War, the civil rights movement, and human rights. They are primarily, but not exclusively, interested in Southern people and Southern settings. They are more likely to publish chapter books than picture books, but will look at the latter if on the subjects mentioned above.

Night Shade Books

307 West 36th Street
11th Floor
New York, NY 10018
(212) 643-6816
www.nightshadebooks.com/contact-us

Story Collection, Horror, New Writers, Fantasy, Novel, Sci fi

This is a very smart publisher who manages to sell books through effective social media marketing. Their authors are getting impressive reviews from *Publishers Weekly* and *Kirkus*. They are an imprint of Skyhorse Publishing and are now accepting submissions through Authors.Me.

www.app.authors.me/#submit/skyhorse-nightshade-books

Prior to submitting, please take a look at their current list.

Nilsen Literary Prize for a First Novel

One University Plaza
MS 2650
Cape Girardeau, MO 63701
www.smsupress.submittable.com/submit

Story Collection, Novella, Novel, New Writers

Publication begins with submitting a manuscript to the Dorothy and Wedel Nilson Literary Prize for a first novel. Authors may submit previously unpublished novels, novellas, and collections of closely linked short stories. The publisher does not consider manuscripts that have been self-published. The competition is open to unpublished novelists who are U.S. residents writing in English.

There is a $25 fee to have the manuscript considered, and the winner will receive a $2000 prize plus publication.

Nine Arches Press

www.ninearchespress.com/submissions.html

Poetry, British

Nine Arches Press now operates via a bi-annual submissions' window for poetry collections. They typically read during the months of April and November.

All submissions must be made through their online Submittable portal. Do not mail or e-mail any submissions to them.

www.ninearchespress.submittable.com/submit

They are currently accepting submissions for both debut collections from new or emerging poets and submissions from established poets with previously published collections.

They have no regional bias; though they are based in the Midlands, they are seriously interested in publishing work from poets nationally.

Nixes Mate

Philip Borenstein
editors@nixesmate.pub
www.nixesmate.pub/submit

Poetry, Story Collection, Novel, Literary Fiction, Literary Magazine

A highly competitive small press, Nixes Mate features small-batch, artisanal literature, created by writers who've been honing their craft the time-honored way: one line at a time.

They like stories. Good stories. Strong stories. Short stories and micro stories. They like narrative and minimalism and words that dance across the page. They like dialogue that is direct and sounds like a real person talking. They believe in Elmore Leonard's Rules of Writing numbers 3 & 4:

- Never use a verb other than "said" to carry dialogue.
- Never use an adverb to modify the verb "said" . . . he admonished gravely.

Poetry should tell a story in language that excites them and grabs them and makes them want to feel ready to fix the world, or destroy it if need be, to defy gravity and end time.

For them, nonfiction combines art and fact with the finest writing. It is a place where memoir and journalism and criticism can meet and have a coffee and discuss the beauty of a maparium without falling for ideology.

They don't like sci-fi, fantasy or horror, but occasionally fancy a good ghost story, or a new take on myths. Just no zombies, dragons, vampires or orcs. When it comes to mysteries and westerns, they have a short attention span. They find blatant erotica boring. If your poetry rhymes for the sake of rhyming, and more importantly rhymes poorly, your work will never find a home at this publisher.

Submit no more than five poems, one short story (no more than 2000 words), two short-short stories (less than 500 words is ideal), or one essay (no more than 3000 words) in the body of an e-mail, or attach a Microsoft Word DOC, DOCX, or RTF file. They insist that you send multiple pieces in a single file. Start each piece on a new page. Add a 50-word or less bio. They allow simultaneous submissions so long as you notify them if your work has been accepted elsewhere.

Though, at this time, they cannot pay anything other than their undying gratitude and appreciation, they ask for first North American serial rights only. Copyright reverts to the author upon publication. Acceptance will be for their quarterly online issues, with consideration for the annual "best of" print edition.

They are now using Submittable to handle their manuscripts. Use e-mail if you would like to send them a query: editors@nixesmate.pub.

No Record Press

inquiry@norecordpress.com
www.norecordpress.com

New Writers, Anthology, Literary Fiction, Novel, Story Collection

No Record Press considers first novels, short-story collections, and books of poetry. They generally do not consider works from authors with previous book publications. Submit only the first 1,000 words of a novel, the first story in a collection, or the first two poems in a book of poetry. If they are interested in evaluating the rest of your work, they will e-mail you with a request for your complete manuscript. If you do not hear back from them within one month, assume that they will be passing on the opportunity to further consider your work. They accept a ridiculously low percentage of submissions for publication. Submit at your own peril.

They prefer to receive e-mail attachments of the Microsoft Word DOC or RTF variety, sent to the following address: inquiry@norecordpress.com. Indicate the type of submission in the subject line of your e-mail, along with the title of your work (for example, "Novel: An Amazing Novel"). A brief bio would be appreciated, but not required.

They no longer publish the *Red Anthology* in printed book form. However, they are considering short story submissions by previously unpublished writers for their online anthology. Submit as in-line text in your e-mail, to inquiry@norecordpress.com. Indicate that it is an anthology submission in the subject line of the e-mail, along with the title (for example, "Anthology: An Amazing Story").

Noemi Press Book Awards
www.noemipress.submittable.com/submit

Story Collection, Novel, Poetry, New Writers, Literary Contest

Founded in 2002, Noemi Press is a 501(c)(3) literary arts organization based in Las Cruces, New Mexico, dedicated to publishing and promoting the work of emerging and established authors and artists. Noemi is housed at New Mexico State University.

Two prizes of $1,000 each and publication by Noemi Press are given annually for one book-length poetry collection and one book-length work of prose. The editors will judge.

- Poets at any stage in their career may submit a manuscript of no more than 90 pages with a $25 entry fee by May 1.
- Prose writers at any stage in their career may submit a manuscript (no page limit) with a $25 entry fee by May 1.

All manuscripts are read anonymously. Strip your manuscript of all identifying material, including dedications and acknowledgements. Otherwise, the manuscript will not be considered. Winners of the prize will receive $1,000 and publication. Use their Submittable portal to enter.

www.noemipress.submittable.com/submit

Nomadic Press
www.nomadicpress.org

New Writers, Poetry, Literary Magazine, Prose Poems, Nonfiction, Hispanic, Children's Books, International

Nomadic Press is proud to print all of their books locally in Oakland, California. They strongly believe in supporting local authors, publishers, and printers, and they believe in growing together. They distribute their books with a local distributor and every week—multiple times a week—feature local writers, musicians, and artists in their diverse events across the Bay Area and Brooklyn, NY. The press is a small, community-focused, non-profit publishing organization.

www.nomadicpress.submittable.com/submit

They wholeheartedly welcome unsolicited submissions for their annual *Nomadic Journal*. They also welcome unsolicited book manuscripts of the following genres: children's, poetry, fiction, nonfiction, or adult. All submissions are handled via Submittable.

Note that their window for submissions runs from January 1 to February 28 every year. They aim to get back to those who have submitted within three months.

North Atlantic Books

Acquisitions Board
2526 Martin Luther King Jr. Way
Berkeley, CA 94704
submissions@northatlanticbooks.com
www.northatlanticbooks.com/submission-guidelines

New Writers, Self-help, Nonfiction

With 1,000 books in print and growing, the list of books they publish is wide-ranging, diverse, and distinguished. As an independent nonprofit 501(c)(3) publisher distributed by Penguin Random House, they enjoy the best of both worlds: complete editorial independence and an unparalleled distribution network.

Visit their online bookstore for an idea of the kinds of books they currently publish: strong categories include bodywork and somatics, ecology and sustainability, food and nutrition, health and healing, indigenous cultures and anthropology, the arts, metaphysics, psychology and personal growth, society and politics, and spirituality and religion. They also offer an imprint dedicated to the martial arts: Blue Snake Books.

If you believe your work would be appropriate for North Atlantic Books, send them a proposal, including a cover letter introducing yourself, together with a brief description of your project, a table of contents, notes on the market you are trying to reach, at least three sample chapters, and a stamped self-addressed envelope if you would like them to return these materials to you. Don't send them original artwork or irreplaceable documents; they cannot assume responsibility for these. You may also e-mail them at the address above.

They are not accepting submissions for new fiction or poetry at this time, and they cannot review submissions of this type. Also note that while some of their publications are trade books with an additional scholarly market, they are not currently accepting submissions for purely academic books.

North Dakota University Press

Dr. Suzzanne Kelley
Editor-in-Chief
NDSU Dept #2360
P.O. Box 6050
Fargo, ND 58108-6050
(701) 231-6848
Suzzanne.Kelley@ndsu.edu
www.ndsu.edu/ahss/ndirs

Memoirs, Creative Nonfiction, Novel, New Writers

The North Dakota State University Press publications' program operates editorially in the manner of a university press, selecting works of merit through peer review. Dr. Suzzanne Kelley, Editor-in-Chief, is the first contact for authors seeking to place book manuscripts for publication with NDSU Press.

Authors are encouraged to submit manuscripts and manuscript proposals through their online submissions' portal. Dr. Kelley may be contacted at North Dakota State University Press at the address above.

When the Editor-in-Chief receives a manuscript from an author, she conducts an internal evaluation and then solicits two authorities in the field to review the manuscript. Based on internal editorial review and external reviewer evaluations, the Editor-in-Chief makes a recommendation as to disposition of the manuscript. The decision may be acceptance (possibly with some revisions expected prior to publication), rejection, or return to author with suggestions for revisions and invitation to re-submit. It is the intention of the Institute to give a decision to the author within four months of submission.

NDSU Press does not consider simultaneous submissions. An author submitting a manuscript to the press signifies thereby that it is not also under consideration at another press. Authors should be prepared to submit a digital (Microsoft Word) version of their work.

www.ndsupress.submittable.com/submit

Northeastern University Press
www.upne.com/staff_acquisitions.html

Nonfiction

This regional university press is part of a consortium of presses. In the past, they have published some fiction, although now, they are not considering it. They're strictly a nonfiction publisher with specific subject areas.

Northeastern University Press brings Northeastern University's distinctive strengths in the humanities and the social sciences to the world of scholarly and general book publishing through its explorations of African-American and women's literature, criminology, music, sports, and Boston culture and history.

The university has earned a reputation as an environment where subject studies have a direct link to the real world and the vibrant urban environment of Boston that Northeastern calls home. Through its rich and diverse publishing program, theory and practice merge, reflecting the core values and identity of the university as a whole. For the names of acquiring editors, see the website above.

Northwestern University Press
Jill L. Petty
TriQuarterly Books/Curbstone Press
629 Noyes Street
Evanston, IL 60208
jill.petty@northwestern.edu
www.nupress.northwestern.edu/content/submissions

International, Nonfiction, Novel, Memoirs, Creative Nonfiction,

TriQuarterly Books imprint is devoted primarily to contemporary American fiction and poetry. Curbstone Books is an innovative and award-winning line of books in fiction, creative nonfiction, memoir, and poetry that promote human rights, social justice, and intercultural understanding. Read their submission guidelines on their website.

Nosy Crow

www.nosycrow.com/

British, Children's Books

Nosy Crow is a new, independent company, publishing children's books and apps. They publish high-quality, commercial fiction and nonfiction books for children aged from 0 to 14 from both well-known authors and illustrators and new talent. They make innovative, multimedia, highly interactive apps for tablets, smart phones and other touchscreen devices. These apps are not existing books squashed onto phones, but instead are specially created to take advantage of the devices to tell stories and provide information to children in new and engaging ways.

Oberlin College Press
www.oberlin.edu/ocpress/

Poetry, Translation

Poetry manuscripts are considered for the Field Poetry Series by invitation only or through entering the annual Field Poetry Prize competition.

Book-length manuscripts of poetry in translation will be considered year-round for the Field Translation Series. Use their submissions' manager to send sample poems and a letter of inquiry describing the work. If you are submitting poems in translation, indicate that you have the author's permission to seek publication for your translations.

Oceanview Publishing
www.oceanviewpub.com/submissions/

Mystery, Crime, Novel, Thriller

Oceanview Publishing specializes in mystery, crime, and thrillers. Do not submit YA or Children's Books. Although authors do not need an agent's representation, the authors must have been previously published.

When the publishers started Oceanview Publishing in 2006, they endeavored to create a tradition of excellence in independent publishing. They love books—and they only publish books they love. Each title they publish is hand-picked, lovingly created, and carefully edited, marketed, and promoted. Now, as one of the fastest growing independent publishers in the U.S., Oceanview is recognized as one of the country's preeminent independent publishers of original mystery, thriller, and suspense titles.

Octavo Editions
www.octavo.com/

Book

Octavo Editions is not a publisher, but they have photographed amazing high-resolution images of rare books. A treat for anyone who writes!

Oklahoma University Press
www.oupress.com/Publish/ForProspectiveAuthors.aspx

Nonfiction

The mission of the University of Oklahoma Press is to publish scholarly books of significance to the state, region, nation, and world, both to convey the results of current research to other scholars and to offer broader presentations for the general public.

Founded in 1928, the University of Oklahoma Press was the first university press established in the Southwest and the fourth founded in the western half of the nation. Over time, the press has grown from a staff of one to a team of more than thirty-five people who work in acquisitions, editing, design and production, marketing and sales, rights, distribution, accounting, and administration.

The University of Oklahoma Press is dedicated to publishing outstanding scholarly works by national and international scholars. The Press's ongoing editorial goal is to maintain its preeminent position as a publisher of books about the West and the American Indian and to expand its program in other scholarly disciplines, including archaeology, classical studies, language and literature (excluding unsolicited fiction and poetry), the natural sciences, political science, and women's studies. Books published by the Press, including those in its series, have accumulated an impressive array of honors and awards. Read details of their submission process on the link above.

Old Mountain Press

2542 S. Edgewater Dr.
Fayetteville, NC 28303
www.oldmp.com/omp.htm

Custom Books

Old Mountain Press (OMP) has assisted hundreds of writers in self-publishing their work. They assist first time authors as well as seasoned writers with several books to their credit. They have had authors as young as 16 and as old as 85. Writers must provide their work, error free, on diskette or as an attached file via e-mail.

Their editors can help ready the manuscript for self-publishing or for submission to an agent, publishing house, or magazine. They also edit everything from short stories and position papers to novels and doctoral dissertations. They do light or heavy editing. They can also recommend someone who will retype your manuscript if it is handwritten or typed, and you don't have it on a computer disk.

Please note that Old Mountain Press is not a vanity press. They do not profess to market the writer's work, but they can advertise the writer's work through their books-in-print page. They will build a web page for your book at no cost and post it in their Books-in-Print section with your ordering information placed on your book's web page. They specialize in low cost, short run (200 minimum), high-quality, perfect-bound books.

Prospective authors can get an estimate by filling out the publisher's online form or by reading their FAQ page and computing the cost using the information provided. Their printer has a wide variety of full-color cover designs. Many of them are at no charge. You can preview the covers on their website.

One World

www.oneworld-publications.com/books/nonfiction/current-affairs.html

International, Nonfiction

One World is not acquiring fiction, children's books, or YA, but they are looking at nonfiction.

They aim to respond to as many submissions as possible; however, due to the sheer number they receive each day, they cannot always guarantee that they will be able to reply to each one. Many proposals are rejected because they do not contain enough information, or because they do not give the right sort of information.

In order to give your project the greatest chance of being considered for publication, read the notes of guidance below and use them to structure what you send:

www.oneworld-publications.com/book-proposals

Oneiric Press

Tracy Atkins
atkins.tracy@gmail.com
www.oneiricpress.org/about-oneiric.html

Poetry, Novel, Literary Fiction

Oneiric Press is a small-press cooperative dedicated to finding and publishing new voices and innovative forms in poetry and prose.

They welcome submissions from new and established writers with an eye towards publishing work that challenges genre or gender boundaries, has a distinctive voice, and takes risks in form and/or content. the Oneiric press team works together to make beautiful, adventurous, intelligent, ground-breaking and high quality books.

E-mail a cover letter and a poetry manuscript of 48-60 pages or a manuscript of 150-300 pages to Tracy Atkins, Publishing Coordinator, at atkins.tracy@gmail.com. Include a short bio and list of publications along with your cover letter and manuscript.

Ooligan Press

www.ooligan.pdx.edu/submissions

Nonfiction, Environmental, Memoirs, Novel, Literary Fiction

A regional publisher with a national focus, Ooligan Press defines the Pacific Northwest as Northern California, Oregon, Idaho, Washington, British Columbia, and Alaska.

They recognize the importance of diversity, particularly within the publishing industry, and are committed to building a literary community that includes traditionally underrepresented voices; therefore, they are interested in works originating from, or focusing on, marginalized communities of the Pacific Northwest. Read their submission guidelines for specifics.

Open Books Press

www.openbookspress.com/query.php

YA Fiction, Memoirs, YA New Adult, Children's Books,

Open Books Press is currently closed to submissions in order to work through their backlog. Subscribe to their e-mail list to be notified when they reopen, or simply check back later.

Open Books Press is dedicated to publishing quality books. When they're open for submissions, they accept adult nonfiction and fiction for all ages (including some YA and children's). All authors with exceptional work will be given serious consideration.

OR Books

267 Fifth Avenue
6th Floor
New York, NY 10016
(212) 414-0054
editor@otherpress.com
www.otherpress.com/about/contact-us

Novel, Literary Fiction, Poetry, Essays, International, Story Collection

Other Press publishes novels, short stories, poetry, and essays from America and around the world that represent literature at its best. E-mail queries to the editor.

Oregon State University Press

121 The Valley Library
Corvallis, OR 97331
www.osupress.oregonstate.edu/for-authors

Nonfiction, Novel, Creative Nonfiction, Essays

Oregon State University Press publishes fiction, creative nonfiction, and essays from authors based in the Northwest. Many of their books have an environmental focus. Other interests include logging and fishing.

Orison Books
www.orisonbooks.submittable.com/submit

Poetry, Nonfiction, Literary Contest, Christian, Literary Fiction, Literary Magazine, Creative Nonfiction, Anthology

Orison Books offers several prizes for publication of stories, poetry, story collections, novels or nonfiction. No strictly religious books, please. They're looking for books or work that spans the boundary between literary fiction/poetry and spirituality. This would not be a good fit for writers of genre fiction.

www.orisonbooks.submittable.com/submit

Each year from December 1—April 1, they accept submissions of full-length poetry (50—100 pages) and fiction (minimum 30,000 words) manuscripts for consideration for The Orison Prizes in Poetry & Fiction. Fiction manuscripts may be a collection of short stories or flash fiction, a novella, or a novel. All manuscripts will be read "blind." (Do not include any identifying information in your manuscript). Original English work only; no translations. Finalists will be selected by the editorial staff at Orison Books, and a winner will be selected in each genre by different prominent writers acting as contest judges.

The entry fee for both contests is $30. The winner in each genre will receive a $1,500 cash prize, publication, and a standard royalties contract. All finalist manuscripts will be considered for publication under a standard royalties contract.

The Orison Anthology Awards in Fiction, Nonfiction, & Poetry offer another publication opportunity. Each year from May 1—August 1 they accept entries of unpublished single works in three genres (fiction, nonfiction, and poetry) for consideration for The Orison Anthology Awards. The winner in each genre will receive a $500 cash prize as well as publication in *The Orison Anthology*, an annual collection of the best spiritually engaged writing that appeared in periodicals the preceding year. (The unpublished work selected for The Orison Anthology Awards will be featured alongside the reprinted material.)

Submit up to 3 poems (10 pp. max), 1 story (up to 8,000 words), or 1 work of nonfiction (up to 8,000 words). You may submit in multiple genres, and/or submit multiple entries in each genre. The entry fee is $15 ($30 if you would like a copy of the anthology).

Fiction manuscript submissions are accepted during the month of October only. They consider all types of fiction, including novels, short story or flash fiction collections, and novellas. The minimum word count is 30,000. Work in English translation is also accepted. (The translator must have permission to publish the translations, or the original work must be in the public domain per U.S. and international copyright law.) When possible, Orison Books offers a small advance against royalties for books selected for publication. Send an author biography and complete manuscript.

Otis Books - Seismicity Editions

www.otis.edu/mfa-writing/otis-books

Fiction, New Writers, Story Collection, Novel, Literary Contest, Literary Fiction

Otis Books is a publication project of MFA Writing at Otis College of Art and Design at the City College of Los Angeles. Their MFA students are involved in all aspects of the press's activities, from selecting and editing manuscripts to designing books, managing production, and getting their titles out into the world. To date Otis Books has published over 40 titles, most recently *Beginnings* by Alan Loney, *The Wilderness After Which* by L.S. Klatt, and *Caesura: Essays* by Gary McDowell. This publisher is open for submissions in the fall.

Outpost 19

Jon Roemer

jon@outpost19.com

www.outpost19.com/about/index.html

Memoirs, Literary Magazine, Poetry, Anthology, Nonfiction, Novella, Story Collection, Novel, Literary Fiction

Outpost 19 publishes novellas, novels, and nonfiction centered around a literary community in Oakland. The publisher has an active reading schedule. They're committed to delivering provocative reading, whether fiction, memoirs, essays, or story collections. They're looking for the artful argument and the story you don't want to stop.

www.outpost19.submittable.com/submit

Their annual anthology of California writing engages a new editor each year.

Owl Canyon Press

Manuscript Submissions
621 Pleasant Street
Boulder, CO 80302
www.owlcanyonpress.com/ocp_books.htm

YA Fiction, Women's Fiction, Contemporary fiction, Historical Fiction, Memoirs, YA Fiction, New Adult, New Writers

Owl Canyon Press asks that prospective authors submit a cover letter that includes the following information:

- Full Name, address, city, phone
- Working Title
- Your target audience
- Genre
- Your primary competitors
- Endorsements
- Estimated word count
- Overview/synopsis
- Available marketing and promotional resources
- Brief biography

Projects should be printed with 1-inch margins and double-spaced. They prefer to receive sample chapters for their initial review rather than a complete manuscript.

E-mail submissions to editors@owlcanyonpress.com.

Send hard copy submissions to the address above. Hardcopy submissions will not be returned without an SASE.

Owl Canyon Press's editorial staff reviews submissions as quickly as they can. Generally, they will review project proposals in 2 to 3 months. However, the workload can vary depending on their project release schedule and the time of year. Allow six months for their editors to complete their review.

Query letters submitted as hard copy are generally reviewed in 1 to 2 months. In rare circumstances reviews can take more time. If you have not heard from them in seven months, contact them.

Owl Hollow Press

www.owlhollowpress.com/submissions

Nonfiction, YA Fiction, Horror, Fantasy, Historical Fiction, Romance, Novel, Sci fi

Olive Hollow Press is open to romantic fantasy, mind-bending science fiction, dark urban paranormal, and horror. They have different readers for each genre, and some like it darker than others, but they're always excited about other worldly adventures for any age group.

From historically-based contemporary to modern love stories, they love to live vicariously through today's teens and tweens. They're not so much interested in books written for contemporary adults, though. They experienced enough midlife malaise in their college English classes, but if you have something you think will interest them, send it anyway! For details, see the website above.

Panhandler

Jonathan Fink
English Dept.
University of West Florida
11000 University Parkway
Pensacola, FL 32514
panhandlermagazine@gmail.com
www.uwf.edu/panhandler

Novel Excerpt, Novella, Creative Nonfiction Essays, Literary Magazine Memoirs, New Writers, Nonfiction, Novel, Poetry

In Spring 2015, *Panhandler Magazine* and the Department of English at University of West Florida launched Panhandler Books. Distributed by the University Press of Florida, Panhandler Books publishes poetry, fiction, and nonfiction consistent with *Panhandler Magazine's* mission to champion underrepresented literary genres. Publishing one book every two years, Panhandler Books provides exceptional attention to the work published in the series.

Writers may also want to submit short stories, poems, or novel excerpts to *Panhandler Magazine*:

www.panhandlermagazine.com/about-2/submit/

Simultaneous submissions are allowed as long as Panhandler is notified immediately if work is accepted elsewhere. The editors read submissions from October 1—March 31.

PANK Press
www.pankmagazine.com/submit-2

Story Collection, Literary Fiction

PANK Books and PANK Magazine are experimental and literary. They're now publishing full length books and chapbooks alongside their print annual magazine and quarterly online offering.

Send them something that screams.

Pantera Press (Australia)
www.panterapress.com.au

Women's Fiction, Fantasy, Historical Fiction, Romance, New Writers, Novel, Literary Fiction, Sci fi, Thriller, YA Fiction, Australian

Pantera Press is one of the few book publishers that not only accepts unsolicited manuscripts but welcomes them. They have spent a long time creating their submissions process, in order to give each submission that they receive the attention it deserves, and importantly, to respond to each author in a respectful period of time. If your work is what they're seeking, they'd be delighted to see it. However, read and follow their submissions guidelines before submitting to them—so that you don't waste your time, their time, and the wait time of other authors submitting to them.

www.panterapress.com.au/fiction-and-nonfiction-how-to-submit

Pantera Press aims to be known as a great new home for Australia's next generation of best-loved authors. That means they want to discover, launch and nurture previously unpublished Australian (and New Zealand) writers who, despite having more than one great book in them, and having a passion for writing, have not yet found the right publisher.

They are seeking books with wide appeal. For both fiction and nonfiction, they are looking for books with bestseller potential and with strong, quality writing and style. For fiction their focus is on mass-market and popular books, that is, great stories that are riveting and well-written. For nonfiction, their focus is on books that foster ideas and debate.

They definitely want to hear from you if you think you might be the next John Grisham, Tim Winton, Jodi Picoult, Kate Grenville, Geraldine Brooks, J.K. Rowling, Stephen King or Jane Green, or if you've written the next *Spotless*, *Freakonomics* or *Tipping Point*.

They are actively looking for Young Adult Fiction, for age group 12 years +. They are not currently publishing picture or illustrated books, cookbooks, self-help books, health and wellness books, travel books, poetry, play scripts, short stories, compilations, novellas, chapter books or children's books.

Parallax Press
www.parallax.org

Self-help, Nonfiction, Children's Books

Socially engaged and with a focus on Buddhism, Parallax Press is a nonprofit publisher, founded and inspired by Zen Master Thich Nhat Hanh. They publish books on mindfulness in daily life and are committed to making these teachings accessible to everyone and preserving them for future generations. They do this work to alleviate suffering and contribute to a more just and joyful world.

www.parallax.org/submission-permission-guidelines/

Parallax Press accepts submissions from both agents and individuals. They accept nonfiction and fiction manuscripts for adults and fiction and nonfiction manuscripts for children. They do not accept poetry at this time.

Their authors include: Thich Nhat Hanh, James Baraz, Bari Tessler, Spring Washam, George Mumford, His Holiness the Dalai Lama, Joanna Macy, Gail Silver, Sulak Sivaraksa, Christopher Willard, and many others. Review current titles before inquiring.

Passager Books

7401 Park Heights Avenue
Baltimore, MD 21208
(410) 837-6047
editors@passagerbooks.com
www.passagerbooks.com/submit

Memoirs, Creative Nonfiction, New Writers, Poetry, Prose Poems

Passager Books is dedicated to authors over 50. They publish two issues of *Passager Journal* each year, as well as a number of books of poetry, short stories, and memoir. Passager Books only publishes manuscripts from authors whose work has appeared in *Passager Journal*. This allows the editors to build a relationship with their authors and the authors' work.

The magazine runs poetry and prose contests, and that is the time to submit. (Poetry Contests are typically published around July/August of each year, and Open Issues around January/February.) Writers must be age 50 or older at the time of publication to submit.

Poets are invited to submit to the Henry Morgenthau Poetry Prize. This prize offers a $3000 prize, plus publication.

Paul Dry Books

Paul Dry
1700 Sansom Street
Suite 700
Philadelphia, PA 19103
(215) 231-9939
pdry@pauldrybooks.com
www.pauldrybooks.com/pages/about-us

Essays, Creative Nonfiction, Literary Fiction, Women's Fiction, Nonfiction, Memoirs

Paul Dry Books is a regional publisher that produces beautiful books. There is no information about how to submit on their website. At Paul Dry Books, their aim is to publish lively books "to awaken, delight, and educate"—and to spark conversation. They publish fiction, both novels and short stories, and nonfiction—biography, memoirs, history, and essays, covering subjects from Homer to Chekhov, bird watching to jazz, New York City to shogunate Japan.

Direct general inquiries to editor@pauldrybooks.com.

Pebblebrook Press

www.stoneboatwi.com/pebblebrook-press.html

Poetry, Memoirs, Novel, Nonfiction

Pebblebook Press is affiliated with *Stoneboat* literary magazine. Their focus is on poetry. Pebblebrook Press publishes 1-2 titles each year. They don't consider unsolicited manuscripts, but if you feel that your project would be a good fit with the Pebblebrook Press catalog, contact them by e-mailing stoneboat.journal@gmail.com. (They are particularly interested in memoir or literary nonfiction as their next project.) If your inquiry piques their interest, they will ask for a proposal or a manuscript excerpt.

Penmore Press

Michael James
920 N. Javalina Pl.
Tucson, AZ 85748
mjames@penmorepress.com
www.penmorepress.typepad.com/submissions

Fantasy, Crime, Historical Fiction, Novel, Mystery, Literary Fiction, Thriller

Penmore Press is an Arizona-based company dedicated to publishing fiction and nonfiction from emerging and established authors. While they welcome most genres of fiction, they are looking for authors who can craft compelling stories, engage them with their prose, and introduce them to intriguing characters. For nonfiction, they look for interesting subjects, impeccable research, and an accessible writing style. They're looking for 90,000- to 150,000-word manuscripts.

Persea Books

90 Broad Street
Suite 2100
New York, NY 10004
www.perseabooks.com/contact

Poetry, Essays, Story Collection, Memoirs, Literary Contest, Creative Nonfiction, Novel, Literary Fiction

Persea Books publishes literary novels and short story collections, creative nonfiction, memoir, essays, biography, literary criticism, books on contemporary issues (multicultural, feminist, LGBTQ), and literary and multicultural anthologies that are assigned in secondary and university classrooms. Their list also includes a small number of Young Adult titles (0-2 per year)—again aimed at the literary reader and the educational market.

Most of all, they are looking for the fresh voice, a clear point of view, and well-written work that will endure. They are pleased to publish debut books and to continue publishing the authors they take on. They do not publish genre fiction (romance, fantasy, science fiction, thrillers), self-help, textbooks, or children's books.

For fiction or nonfiction submissions, send query letters by USPS. Include a cover letter, author background and publication history, a synopsis of the proposed work, and a sample chapter. Indicate if the work is simultaneously submitted. Send to the address above and include an SASE for return of materials.

Submissions may also be sent via e-mail. If they're interested they will respond: info@perseabooks.com.

Phoneme Media

submissions@phonememedia.org
www.phonememedia.org/submissions

Translation, Women, Novel

Phoneme Media is a good publisher for authors whose first language is not English. They have some great looking covers. This isn't a big publisher, so don't expect to make a great deal of money!

www.phonememedia.org/artists/

Phoneme Media accepts submissions of world literature manuscripts in translation year round, and the publisher is particularly interested in work from speakers of non-Indoeuropean languages and by women.

To submit, send a cover letter summarizing the project and its importance, a ten-to-twenty page excerpt, and biographical notes for the original author and translator to submissions@phonememedia.org.

Include information about copyright ownership in your cover letter. Response time is typically 8 to 12 weeks. Do not query regarding the status of the manuscript before that time has elapsed.

Pink Narcissus Press

www.pinknarc.com/submissions.html

Novella, Horror, Sci fi, Fairy Tales, Fantasy, Steampunk

Heroic quests. Epic battles between good and evil. Worlds populated with monsters, errant knights, faerie folk, demons, wizards and dragons. These are all fine things in this publisher's opinion, and they seek out the original in the traditional.

However, even they sometimes tire of hanging around in the cold, damp castle until the king sends readers off on another quest for another magic sword. Therefore dark fantasy, urban fantasy, literary fantasy, and crossovers with science fiction and horror are also welcome.

Other genres they like served straight up include horror, the new weird, steampunk, and soft sociological science fiction. They consider themselves LGBT friendly and welcome themes of alternative sexuality. Pink Narcissus is a small press publisher founded in 2010.

Plays Inverse

submissions@playsinveerse.com
www.playsinverse.com/contact.html

Plays

This publisher is seeking Full Lengths, One-Acts, Monologues, Dialogues, Trialogues, Trial-logs, Translations, Collaborations, Devisations, Divinations, 10-Minute Plays, 10-Second Plays, 10-Year Plays, Comedies, Tragedies, Dragedies, Satires, Satyrs, History Plays, Herstory Plays, Itstory Plays, Verse Plays, Performance Poetry, Radio Plays, Cardio Plays, Choreographies, Micro-Plays, Macro-Plays, Found Plays, Flash Plays, Alt Plays, Conventional Plays, Conversational Plays, Conversion Plays, Vanity Plays, Closet Drama, Closeted Drama, Adaptations, Screenplays, Regional Plays, I-Guess-I'll-Call-This-A Plays, Melodrama, Mellowdrama, Mallowdrama, Slapstick, Vaudeville, Mime Routines, Overheard Conversations, Fashion Advice, Fan Fiction, D&D Play Sessions, Plays-Within-Plays, Plays-Without-Plays, Play-Like Things, Drama, etc.

PM Press

P.O. Box 23912
Oakland, CA 94623
www.pmpress.org/content/article.php/submit

Nonfiction, Novel

PM Press publishes everything from noir to science fiction to important (if sometimes neglected) theory to thought-provoking books on pirates and punk rock.

So you've looked at their site and think you'd be a good fit? Well, then what they would like you to do is write them a letter detailing what you've written, and tell them why you're a fit. And because they need to sell books to be sustainable and take on new projects, tell them who the audience for your book is, and how you can help reach them.

Talk yourself up here, and let them know why you think this book is important and why other people will agree with you!

And finally, send them a little sample of what you've written, but all they need is a taste! They definitely don't need anything more than a chapter. Maybe two, but only if they're short. Take a look at the list above, and make sure you have everything that applies to your book.

They also do music, CDs, etc.

Possibilities Publishing Company
www.possibilitiespublishingcompany.com/how-it-works

Essays, Memoirs, Novel, Creative Nonfiction

For this publisher, fiction should have a strong narrative arc, interesting and relatable characters, realistic dialogue, and for the love of Plato, something needs to *happen*. *Unfit* has a 4.5-star rating on Amazon because the story moves quickly and has unexpected turns while also painting clear pictures that let you feel as though you are in the scenes. The most common sentiment in the reviews of *Wissahickon Souls* is how clear and engaging the writing was and how connected readers felt to the characters.

They will publish previously published works, as long as the rights have reverted back to you. They publish both e-books and trade paperbacks.

They don't offer advances. They will, however, do everything in their power to help you sell as many books as possible and raise your profile as an author. They're partners in this endeavor, and their success is linked to yours.

They're also interested in creative nonfiction. Whether it's a memoir, a collection of essays, or a series of blog entries, creative nonfiction should be compelling, have a narrative arc, be well written, and be about something universal. *Freak Show Without a Tent* is a collection of essays about one family's crazy vacations, but it's also a story about fathers and sons and family relationships in general. Those are universal themes that even non-adventure-travel fans can relate to, and that's why it was selected for the Travel Channel's Summer 2014 Reading list.

Press 53

Kevin Morgan Watson
560 N. Trade Street
Winston-Salem, NC 27130
(336) 414-5599
surrealsouth@gmail.com
www.press53.submittable.com/submit

Story Collection, Poetry, Literary Contest, Literary Magazine, Memoirs, New Writers

The Press 53 Award for Short Fiction identifies one short fiction collection for a cash prize and publication. This is an award for an outstanding, unpublished collection of short stories by a U.S.-based author, regardless of the author's publishing history. This contest runs from September-December each year with the winning entry earning publication, a $1000 advance and publication the following October.

The Press 53 Award for Poetry (opens April 1) os similar to the short fiction contest. This contest runs from April-July each year. The winner will be selected by Press 53 poetry series editor, Tom Lombardo, and will be published as a Tom Lombardo Poetry Selection.

They have additional contests for poems, flash fiction, and short stories. Authors who do not enter their contests can gain their attention by publishing widely in journals and magazines, by winning or placing in other contests (they keep an eye on who is winning and placing in a number of contests), and by becoming involved in the literary community. They are always looking for voices that connect with readers on a variety of levels.

Prolific Press

www.prolificpress.com/Manage-Submissions/index.php

Poetry, Novel, Nonfiction

Prolific Press is now accepting full-length poetry, fiction, and nonfiction manuscripts for book publishing (no sample chapters please).

They do not charge reading fees. Decisions are based on several factors, including the popularity of the author, the market for similar books at the time of distribution, and the features of the book including quality, size, and genre. Emerging authors are welcome to submit.

Full publishing comes with a token cash advance and a standard royalty contract. Prolific Press covers publishing costs and distribution of the book. The title is sold in the Prolific Press store and added to distribution chains, such as Amazon.com, Baker & Taylor, Barnes & Noble, NACSCORP, Espresso Book Machine and many others, totaling more than thirty thousand retailers. Each publishing contract is different.

To submit a manuscript, please send the full manuscript in Word format. (No sample chapters please.)

Name your file like this: Smith1 (last name followed by the number of submissions you have sent). If this is your first submission to Prolific Press, then follow your last name with the number 1. Also, send the following:

- Your real name
- Your pen name (if any)
- Your biography
- Number of words or pages
- Your real physical address (not work or P.O. Box)
- Your mailing address (if different)
- Your e-mail address
- Your phone number
- How you plan to market your book

Lastly, please let us know why you chose Prolific Press.

Pski's Porch Publishing

pskisporch@gmail.com
www.pskisporch.com/?page_id=24

New Writers, Novel, Novella, Poetry

This publisher started Pski's Porch Publishing because they love books and good writing, and because the world of contemporary publishing has some structural problems that prevent a lot of good work from getting published, problems that seem to have worsened with corporate consolidation. Small presses have long existed to counteract the effects of mainstream publishing culture, and they are happy to be part of that tradition. Buy a book or two, send them your work, and keep reading.

Rare Bird Books

453 S. Spring St.
Suite 302
Los Angeles, CA 90013
(213) 623-1773
info@rarebirdlit.com
www.rarebirdbooks.com

Self-Publishing, Essays, Creative Nonfiction, Historical Fiction, Literary Fiction, Novel,

Rare Bird is the parent company of Rare Bird Books and Rare Bird Lit, two Los Angeles-based book industry firms founded by former Book Soup marketing and publicity director Tyson Cornell.

They do not consider unsolicited manuscripts, but they do help authors with design, publicity, and marketing. For information on these services, please contact them via e-mail, and your query will be directed to the appropriate representative.

Red Bridge Press

www.redbridgepress.com/submissions.html

Literary Magazine, Poetry, New Writers, Nonfiction, Novel, Prose Poems, Literary Fiction, Creative Nonfiction

They publish books and an online journal dedicated to writing that breaks free from the confines of mainstream realism to surprise, delight, and challenge readers.

Send work that is not easily classifiable in form or content, work that is fearless and surprising, that jumps off cliffs and soars. Send writing that is literary in its attention to language without being stuffy or safe. If your prose reads like poetry, there's sur- in your realism, or your work otherwise does not fit neatly into any of the usual boxes, then we'd like to see it.

We are not looking for work that is primarily aimed at a genre audience (i.e., high fantasy, hard science fiction, horror, romance, or erotica). However, if, for example, your work would be rejected by a science fiction or fantasy editor because the style is too experimental or rejected by a literary editor because the protagonist is a sentient asteroid, then it is what we are looking for.

They publish new book-length works of literary fiction, poetry, and nonfiction, including novels and collections of short pieces. Sign up for their e-mail newsletter, and they'll let you know when the next reading period opens and how to submit your work.

Red Empress Publishing

www.redempresspublishing.com/submissions

Fantasy, Historical Fiction, New Writers, Novel, Mystery, Story Collection

Red Empress publishes romance, mystery, fantasy, and historical fiction. They're looking for submissions by women, submissions by people of color, and new authors.

Previously published works that are available for reprint, especially Gothic romances from 1960-1980, are especially welcome. (Digital files are not required for these types of submissions. If you only have physical copies of your out-of-print book, e-mail them for more information.)

Short story collections and anthologies can also be submitted. (No stand-alone short stories at this time).

The total word count must be at least 50,000 words for all submissions.

Red Hen Press
www.redhen.org/contact-2/submission-guidelines

Linked Stories, Nonfiction, Poetry Story Collection, Memoirs, Literary Contest, Novel, Literary Fiction

This is a prestigious press that specializes in literary writing. They have three contests a year in poetry, nonfiction, and fiction. Red Hen Press is proud to confer four annual literary awards: the Benjamin Saltman Poetry Award for $3,000, a four-week PLAYA Residency, and the publication of a full manuscript; the Red Hen Press Fiction Award; and the Red Hen Press Nonfiction Award, each for $1000 and publication; and the Red Hen Press Women's Prose Prize for $1000, and publication of a full-length manuscript by Red Hen Press.

www.redhenpress.submittable.com/submit

Red Hen Press is an independent, non-profit press that publishes about twenty books of fiction, nonfiction, and poetry every year. They're looking for novels, memoir, creative nonfiction, hybrid works, and story, essay, and poetry collections of exceptional literary merit that demonstrate a high level of mastery.

Red Hen publications are diverse in style and subject, but tend to have in common a certain wildness. Familiarize yourself with their catalog before submitting. Representative fiction writers include Ron Carlson, Brian Doyle, B.H. James, Andrew Lam, David Maine, Ellen Meeropol, and Rob Roberge. Representative poets include Chris Abani, Katharine Coles, Camille Dungy, Eloise Klein Healy, Douglas Kearney, David Mason, Peggy Shumaker, and William Trowbridge.

Red Mountain Press

P.O. Box 32205
Santa Fe, NM 87594
(505) 986-9774
redmtnpress@gmail.com
www.redmoujntainpress.us

Literary Contest, Poetry, Novel, Literary Fiction

Fiction submissions are closed for the moment, but this publisher has a poetry prize. The Red Mountain Prize for Poetry awards $1000 and publication of a full-length book of poetry. The most important criterion is that the manuscript manifests significant themes in beautiful, strong and evocative language.

   www.redmountainpress.us/poetry-prize/

Redbat Books

info@redbatbooks.com
www.redbatbooks.com/submissions.html

Poetry, Nonfiction, Essays, Novel

Based in the Pacific Northwest, Redbat Books has a preference for authors from that region. As a small press, they are committed to offering advocacy and dedication to every author and work they represent, but this does limit their publishing capabilities.

They have recently received an overwhelming number of submissions and are doing their best to respond in a timely manner. For specifics of their submissions' requirements, please see the website above.

Reliquary Press

submissions@reliquarypress.com
www.reliquarypress.com/Reliquary_Press/Submissions.html

Novel, Fantasy, Horror, Sci fi, New Writers

They are currently looking for work in the Sci-Fi, Fantasy, and Horror genres. Stories published by Reliquary should make readers feel strongly about the characters and the outcome of the story. They should bring the reader to worlds they will not want to leave. And they should tell stories that pull the reader in.

~248~

Rescue Press

www.rescuepress.co/submissions

Poetry, Story Collection, Novel, Creative Nonfiction, Literary Contest, Literary Fiction

Rescue Press reads submissions twice a year. In June, they read for the Black Box Poetry Prize, a contest for full-length collections of poetry, open to poets at any stage in their writing careers. In January, they read for their Open Prose Series, which publishes one work a year of nonfiction, fiction, or sui generis prose and aims to support the wider discussion of contemporary literary prose. To receive notifications for these contests, join their mailing list.

Rescue Press is an independent publisher of chaotic and investigative work, founded in the winter of 2009. They publish work by activists, artists, craftsmen, list-makers, philosophers, poets, scientists, writers, and creative thinkers of all kinds. They're interested in collections of artwork, comics, essays, experiments, how-tos, interrogations, manifestos, notes, poetry, stories, and anything else that transforms lives.

Restless Books

232 3rd Street
Suite A111
Brooklyn, NY 11215
www.restlessbooks.com/prize-for-new-immigrant-writing

Journalism, International, Nonfiction, Essays, Memoirs, Literary Contest, New Writers, Novel, Travel Narratives, Creative Nonfiction

Restless Books publishes an outstanding debut literary work by a first-generation immigrant. The prize is to be awarded for fiction and nonfiction in alternating years. Submissions for the Prize open every Fall. The winner receives $10,000 and publication by Restless Books.

Restless Books is an independent, nonprofit publisher devoted to championing essential voices from unexpected places and vantage points, whose stories cross linguistic and cultural borders. They seek extraordinary international literature that feeds their restlessness: their curiosity about the world, passion for other cultures and languages, and eagerness to explore beyond the confines of the familiar. Their books—fiction, narrative nonfiction, journalism, memoirs, travel writing, and young people's literature—offer readers an expanded understanding of a changing world.

Resurrection House

www.resurrectionhouse.com/submissions.php

Novel, Sci fi, Mystery, Horror, Fantasy

Resurrection House is always keen on previously unpublished novel-length works of science fiction, fantasy, dark fantasy, and noir mystery with a tinge of otherworldliness—and the occasional bit of horror. They are not terribly rigorous in their definitions of these genres. They prefer character-driven pieces, but don't mind being kept up late due to a tightly wound, plot-driven book. Their interest is piqued by material that is not strictly beholden to the history of and/or culture of Western European civilization.

Send a query to editors@resurrectionhouse.com and include a brief cover letter that tells them a little bit about yourself and your book. Include the full manuscript as an attachment in an industry standard text file format (PDF is acceptable, as well). Give them six weeks before querying as to the status of your submission.

Submissions thrown over the transom (real or virtual) or sent through the business contact address may get waylaid, misfiled, or outright tossed.

Richard Sullivan Prize in Fiction

233 Decio Hall
Dept. of English
University of Notre Dame
Notre Dame, IN 46556
www.english.nd.edu/creative-writing/publications/sandeen-sullivan-prizes

Literary Contest, Story Collection, Poetry, Novella

The Sullivan Prize in Short Fiction and the Sandeen Prize in Poetry are awarded to authors who have published at least one previous volume of short fiction or poetry. If the book was self-published, it does not meet their requirements. Vanity press publications also do not fulfill this requirement. To verify eligibility, include a photocopy of the copyright and the title page of the previous volume.

Submit two copies of the manuscript and inform them if the manuscript is available electronically. Mail manuscripts to the address above. Include an SASE for acknowledgment of receipt of your submission. If you would like your manuscript returned, send an SASE. Manuscripts will not otherwise be returned. A $15 administrative fee should accompany submissions. Make checks payable to University of Notre Dame. Every contestant will receive a one-year free subscription to the *Notre Dame Review*.

The volumes of the Sandeen/Sullivan Prizes will be published in trade paperback format. There will be a $1,000 prize, a $500 award and a $500 advance against royalties from the Notre Dame Press. Submissions for the Sullivan Prize can be sent July 1-31. Submissions for the Sandeen Prize should be sent May 1-September 1.

Rose Metal Press

Kathleen Rooney
P.O. Box 1956
Brookline, MA 02446
www.rosemetalpress.com/Submit/Submit.html

Prose Poems, Fiction, Literary Contest, Chapbook

Rose Metal Press is an independent publisher of hybrid genres. The press has an open reading period from June 1 to June 30. During that period, they will be seeking full-length hybrid and cross-genre manuscripts. They are interested in short short, flash, and micro-fiction; prose poetry; novels-in-verse or book-length linked narrative poems; flash nonfiction or book-length memoirs-in-shorts; fragmentary works and book-length lyric essays; image and text collaborations and other collaborative work; and other literary works that move beyond traditional genres to find new forms of expression.

The best way to see what they mean by hybrid is to take a look at their catalog. They welcome submissions in all styles and on all subjects, and encourage a broad and expansive interpretation of hybridity. Surprise them with your innovation!

Manuscripts should be 48 pages or more. If individual pieces or excerpts of a project have been published in journals or elsewhere, include that information in an acknowledgments page. Also, feel free to include an author bio. Submissions will be accepted through their Submittable site with a $15 reading fee.

Roundabout Press

P.O. Box 370310
West Hartford, CT 06137
www.roundaboutpress.com

Story Collection, Novel

Roundabout Press is always looking for fiction manuscripts. Their primary concern is literary excellence. If you have a book that you would like them to consider, feel free to contact the editor by regular mail with the first 20 pages, a one- or two-page query letter and a self-addressed stamped envelope. Mail it to the address above.

Route (U.K. Publisher)

P.O. Box 167
Pontefract, West Yorkshire
United Kingdom WF8 RWW
01 (977) 793442
info@route-online.com
www.route-online.com/submissions

Story Collection, British, Novel, Literary Fiction

They are a small but dedicated team who give a lot of care and attention to the books they publish. They only take on a handful of titles per year at most, even less from open submissions, and need to be convinced that books they commission are within their remit, that they can add value and are viable enough to support through sales.

They don't guarantee to reply to all submissions. They will reply if they want to see more. If you submit by post, include an SASE if you want them to return your work.

Founded in 2000, Route is a terraced publishing house in the north of England. The principle commitment is to authentic stories and good books. Route publishes stories in print, audio and digital forms, creating books one way or another.

"The sharpest, on the button writing you'll read all year. Route could soon start taking on a Samizdat level of importance as it quietly ushers in the beginnings of a much needed literary renaissance."—*The Big Issue*

"Now they rely on small independent publishers such as Route, often based outside London, to support authors such as Michael Nath. Two or three decades ago, a novel this unusual would not have seemed out of place on, say, Picador's list."—*The Independent*

Run Amok Books

J.H. Kim

www.runamokbooks.com/

www.runamokbooks.com/submissions.html

New Writers, Nonfiction, Essays, Literary Fiction, Creative Nonfiction

Although this press is periodically closed to submissions, they will reopen and are open to unagented authors. In nonfiction, they are looking for humorous memoirs and other types of creative nonfiction. They would love to see a collection of essays. They are also interested in solidly researched, more traditional nonfiction that is off the beaten path. Please no cookbooks, and nothing related to health, spirituality, or religion. In fiction, they'll look at just about anything. However, keep in mind that they are generally not fans of vampires, zombies, or anything that involves magic wands. When they reopen, send submissions to submissions@runamokbooks.com.

Send a detailed synopsis and table of contents, along with the first 25 pages of your finished manuscript to the e-mail address above. Please send these three documents as Word OC, DOCX, or PDF files, and send them as attachments. Please put your name somewhere in the document names, so the editors can determine to whom the document belongs. They will respond with an initial e-mail to let you know they have received your submission. A final decision can take anywhere between 2 weeks and 6 months.

If the manuscript is accepted for publication, Run Amok will take care of all aspects of the book's publication at no cost to you. In a word, they do not charge authors anything for their services. However, they do expect authors to be strong participants in the promotion of their books, and authors who already have an online presence/platform will be given priority. Cash advances are generally reserved for authors who have a proven track record with previously published books, and to be fully transparent, these cash advances are small and meant to be more a gesture of goodwill than anything else.

Saddle Road Press

www.saddleroadpress.com/submissions.html

Essays, Story Collection, Literary Fiction, Memoirs, Novel, Nonfiction

Saddle Road Press opens for submissions once a year. Sign up for their e-mail to be notified when they are open again. They are primarily looking for work that moves and delights them, whatever it is.

They are interested in poetry, literary fiction, memoir and essays, and hope to expand their offerings from the Pacific coasts of the Americas, the islands of the Pacific, Australia and New Zealand.

They pay royalties but do not offer an advance. They provide basic marketing for their books, but expect their authors to take an active role in marketing and promotion.

Santa Fe Writers Project Awards

369 Montezuma Ave
Suite 350
Santa Fe, NM 87501
sfwritersproject@gmail.com
www.sfwp.com/the-contest

Linked Stories, Novel-in-Progress, Nonfiction, Essays, Novella, Novel, Literary Contest, Fiction, New Writers, Creative Nonfiction

Their awards are open to everyone over the age of 18, and international entries are welcome. You and your entry do not need to be associated with New Mexico; they publish a wide variety of fiction and nonfiction globally. However, be advised that there is a $35 entry fee for the award.

What are they looking for? All fiction and creative nonfiction will be eligible despite genre, form, subject, or length. They'll take full-length manuscripts, works-in-progress, collections short or long, and essays. They don't care about what the big presses believe to be "marketable." Instead, they want to see excellence in writing, no matter the form it takes. Past winners have ranged from flash fiction to memoir to magical realism to literary fiction to cultural essays.

The length of the entry is not an issue. There's no minimum or maximum. In addition to them publishing your work, winners will receive a grand prize is $1,500, and two runners-up will receive $1,000 each. Authors retain all rights to their work.

Previously published material is also eligible as long as it has not been published by a major press. You can submit if you have published in zines, lit journals, and with small indie presses. Self-published books are eligible, as are books published via Amazon's CreateSpace, KDP, etc.

If you have published with a small press and have not received any marketing support, then your book is eligible. The standard industry cut-off for marketing support (advertising, publicity, etc.) is $5000-$10,000.

Savant Books and Publications LLC

www.savantbooksandpublications.com/contact.php

Poetry, Anthology, Novel, Historical

Authors submitting to this press must have a U.S. Social Security Number. Savant Books and Publications (SBAP) seeks the best in enduring literary (book/e-book), audio (CD) and audio-video (DVD) works "with a twist" that expand readers', listeners', and/or viewers' points-of-view and world outlook. They also publish a poetry anthology.

As far as novels are concerned, they are interested in all genres, but especially historical or alternative history fiction. In the nonfiction realm, they'll consider memoirs, academic these and dissertations (but rewritten for the general public). They will also consider textbooks and workbooks, especially those involving or invoking transformational learning.

SBAP only accepts never-before-published, solicited and non-solicited manuscripts, audio works and audio-video works. SBAP accepts works with both established and previously unpublished authors, recording artists or audio-video producers. SBAP does not require that the submitter be represented by an agent.

Schaffner Press

Tim Schaffner
P.O. Box 41567
Tucson, AZ 85717
tim@schaffnerpress.com
www.schaffnerpress.com/submissions

Literary Contest, Poetry, Essays, Creative Nonfiction, Nonfiction, Crime, Historical Fiction, Memoirs, Novel, Literary Fiction, Story Collection

This press asks that you query first. In fiction they're interested in literary adult fiction, short fiction collections, historical with socially relevant content, and crime fiction. In nonfiction, they'll consider memoir, autobiography, and biography. The manuscript length should fall between 60,000 and 100,000 words.

As an independent publisher, they look for books that will stand the test of time. Their publishing mission statement is to find "Books of Social Relevance for the Discerning Reader."

Scribe

2 John Street
London, England
United Kingdom WC1N 2ES
44 (0) 20 34054218
submissions@scribepub.com.au
www.scribepublications.com.au/about-us/manuscript-policy

Creative Nonfiction, Nonfiction, British, Australian, Novel, Literary Fiction

This publisher has two reading periods for submissions: March 1-March 21 and September 1-September 21. This is a small press in Australia and London. Follow their instructions for e-mailing your query. To submit you must have a previous publication history.

They publish books that matter—narrative and literary nonfiction on important topics, and the best of local, international, and translated fiction.

If you are a fiction writer not represented by a literary agent, they are only able to consider unsolicited submissions if you have a demonstrated background of publishing for general readers (for example, by having had books published by trade publishers, or by having short stories published in literary journals or magazines), or if you have received awards or commendations for your writing, or if you have a recommendation from a published author.

Note that, at present, they do not accept unsolicited poetry, plays, young adult fiction, individual short stories, or children's picture books.

If you meet the eligibility criteria, do not call, but e-mail your proposal to submissions@scribepub.com.au within one of their open submission periods noted above. Include the title of the work in the e-mail subject line and whether it is a fiction or nonfiction submission. For specifics of their requirements, see their submissions' page.

Second Story Press

20 Maud Street
Suite 401
Toronto, ON
Canada M5V 2M5
www.secondstorypress.ca/submissions

YA Fiction, Women, Children's Books, Canadian, Essays, Novel

They are a Canadian feminist press publishing books of special interest to women, and they do not consider works by American authors. Their list is a mix of fiction, nonfiction, and books for young readers. They look for manuscripts dealing with the many diverse and varied aspects of the lives of girls and women, as well as social justice, diversity, and children's empowerment.

If you are interested in submitting, they strongly suggest that you familiarize yourself with the books they have published in the past. If you feel that your manuscript fits with their list, send it according to their instructions.

If you are an American author or illustrator, you should consider sending your manuscript or artwork to one of the many U.S. publishing houses. SSP focuses on Canadian authors (either citizens or permanent residents of Canada). They rarely make exceptions to this rule, which pertains to other international authors and illustrators as well.

Note that they do not publish poetry, short story collections, traditional romance novels, rhyming picture books, or books with anthropomorphized animals. Also keep in mind that as a feminist press, they are looking for non-sexist, non-racist, and non-violent stories.

Serena McDonald Kennedy Award

Snake Nation Press
110 West Force Street
Valdosta, GA 31601
snake.nation.press@gmail.com
www.snakenationpress.org/snakenation

Linked Stories, New Writers, Story Collection, Novella, Literary Contest, Chapbook, Literary Magazine, Poetry

Snake Nation Press publishes books in conjunction with two literary contests. The Violet Reed Haas Prize for Poetry offers a $1000 prize + publication for a 50-75 page poetry manuscript.

The Serena McDonald Kennedy Award offers a $1000 award and publication for a 50,000 word novella or 200-page manuscript of short stories. Previously published works may be entered. An entry fee of $25 must accompany the submission.

Mail the manuscript to the address above, or send a check and e-mail the entry. The deadline for both contests is December 31.

Seven Stories Press

140 Watts Street
New York, NY 10013
(212) 226-8760
sevenstories@sevenstories.com
www.sevenstories.com

YA Fiction, Essays, Hispanic

Under the direction of publisher Dan Simon, perhaps no other small independent house in America has consistently attracted so many important voices away from the corporate publishing sector. In 1999, Seven Stories was named the fastest growing independent publisher in America by *Publishers Weekly*, and in 2000, the second fastest growing.

They publish works of the imagination and political titles by voices of conscience under their primary imprint.

In addition to their main imprint, the publisher has two other imprints. Triangle Square is their newest imprint is for the next generation: a new breed of skeptical young readers. A second new imprint is *Siete Cuentos*. This Spanish-language imprint represents a major ongoing effort to introduce important English-language texts to new readers.

Due to the overwhelming number of submissions they have received they are currently unable to accept entire unsolicited manuscripts. However, you may still send a query letter and two sample chapters. Authors with a track record of publishing will have a better chance of success.

Shade Mountain Press

P.O. Box 11393
Albany, NY 12211
publisher@shademountainpress.com
www.shademountainpress.com/contact.php

Women, Novel, New Writers, Literary Fiction

Currently on hiatus, but with a solid track record and the likelihood of reopening, Shade Mountain Press is committed to publishing literature by women, especially women from marginalized/underrepresented communities. They seek literary fiction that's politically engaged, that challenges the status quo and gender/class/race privilege. They look for work that's wise, raucous, joyful, angry, alive. Both realism and its various alternatives (magic realism / fabulism / slipstream / the fantastic / dystopianism) are welcome, as long as the work is literary rather than genre fiction.

Before you submit a manuscript to them, ask yourself, as the medieval theologians did, "Is it good? Is it true? Is it beautiful?"

As a feminist press, Shade Mountain is committed to publishing literature by women, especially women of color, women with disabilities, women from working-class backgrounds, and LGBTQ women. They publish work that's politically engaged, challenges the status quo, and tells the stories that usually go unheard.

They've released one to two books a year since 2014. Their title *White Light*, the debut novel by Vanessa Garcia, was named to NPR's Best Books of 2015. Shade Mountain's books are available on their website and through Small Press Distribution, as well as bookstores and online retailers.

Shadow Mountain Publishing

Lisa Mangum
Managing Editor
www.shadowmountain.com/submit-your-manuscript

YA Fiction, Women's Fiction, Fantasy, Romance, Novel, Christian, Fairy Tales, Family

Shadow Mountain Publishing is passionate about clean content and empowering values. They publish general fiction and nonfiction for all ages, all genres. They have a strong interest in middle grade fantasy and clean romance. They also publish a limited number of manuscripts in specialized genres including children's picture books, family and parenting, and self-help. They are not interested in the following genres: business and finance, family histories/personal journals, or poetry.

Their Ensign Peak imprint specializes in books that are religious in nature but that are intended for a general, nondenominational audience. Submit manuscripts intended for this imprint through Shadow Mountain Publishing.

Allow twelve to fourteen weeks for the editors to complete the review process and reply to you with their decision. They use Submittable to handle their submissions.

www.deseretbook.submittable.com/submit/59544/shadow-mountain-submissions

Shotgun Honey

www.shotgunhoney.com/submissions

New Writers, Novella, Crime, Novel

Since 2011, Shotgun Honey has been a steady outlet for crime, noir, and hard-boiled flash fiction. Their website has featured over 400 writers and has published nearly a thousand stories, all told within a mere 700 words. If you want to be part of their growing imprint and have a novella or short novel between 25,000 and 50,000 words, or a collection of short stories with a crime fiction slant, they want to hear from you. They have a limited submissions' period, so check back if they happen to be closed.

Silver Empire

Russell Newquist
Morgan Newquist
www.silverempire.org/submissions

Anthology, Fantasy, Novel, Sci fi, YA, Steampunk

Silver Empire publishes sci fi, fantasy, and space operas from 60,000-150,000 words. Their goal is to publish the best heroic, wondrous, adventure fiction out there and to support authors who want to build their careers through joint marketing efforts, giveaways, and newsletter swaps.

They want stories that showcase heroism, and they enjoy fiction that dares to write about wonders they've never imagined. Their submission deadline opens and closes, depending on their backlog. They also have anthologies for sci fi and fantasy with rolling admissions. Contact the publishers via e-mail if you think your manuscript is a good fit: support@authorsmakemoney.com.

Sirens Call

www.sirenscallpublications.com

Literary Magazine, Fantasy, Novella, Crime, Horror, Novel, Mystery, Thriller

Sirens Call Publications is open to everyone: pre-published works, online serials, and Indie authors. If you have a tale to tell, they want to read it. The submissions period opens and closes, depending on the volume of submissions.

They are an edgy/dark fiction publisher interested in stories of horror, fantasy, science fiction, mystery and suspense. If your work falls outside one of those genres and you believe that Sirens Call Publications is a good fit for you, feel free to give them a try. They are a co-operative of writers with many varied tastes and styles, and while your piece may not fall into one of their main categories, it doesn't mean that they won't consider working with you on it.

It is their policy at Sirens Call Publications not to publish any material containing sexual content involving minors in any way, stories containing human bestiality (submissions pertaining to werewolves and other supernatural creatures are excluded from the use of the term bestiality), or stories containing overtly descriptive/graphic rape scenes; other than that, the only boundaries are your imagination!

Sexual content unnecessary to the storyline is discouraged unless you are submitting an erotic story for consideration. Gore for the sake of gore or simply included for shock value in a piece is discouraged as well, and will most likely not garner their attention unless it is necessary to support the storyline.

Skyhorse Publishing
307 West 36th Street
11th Floor
New York, NY 10018
(212) 643-6816
www.skyhorsepublishing.com

Novel, Children's, Nonfiction, Humor

Skyhorse Publishing, one of the fastest-growing independent book publishers in the United States. Over the course of its ten-year history, Skyhorse has had forty-three titles on the *New York Times'* bestseller lists.

Skyhorse publishes a maverick list that includes fiction, nonfiction, history, politics, rural living, cooking, humor, and children's books. Following in the footsteps of its parent company, Sky Pony's goal is to provide books for readers with a wide variety of interests. Its continually growing list includes fiction, picture books, educational books, novelty books, and reissues of well-loved classics.

They are open to receiving submissions for proposed books in the following categories: Sports (Team and Individual); Outdoor Sport (Hunting, Fishing, and Camping); Adventure and Travel; Health and Fitness; House and Home; History; Humor; Military History; Business; Games and Gambling; Horses; Pets and Animals; Nature and Science; Food and Wine; Aviation; True Crime; and Current Events.

Before submitting a proposal, they suggest you click around their site and take a look at the kinds of books they've published. This will help you gain an idea of what they're looking for.

A nonfiction book proposal consists of:

- A brief query (cover) letter
- A one-to-two page synopsis
- An annotated chapter outline
- Market analysis, including competitive research
- A sample chapter or two

Include your curriculum vitae (bio) as well as a list of all previous publishing credits. If they are interested in seeing more than the first 50 pages, they will contact you and request the balance of the manuscript.

Send all submissions to submissions@skyhorsepublishing.com. In the subject line of your submission, include only one of the following categories:

- Outdoor & Sports
- Fiction & Literary Nonfiction
- Children's
- Cooking & Lifestyle
- Politics, History, & General Nonfiction
- Racehorse (highly trending topics; e.g. adult coloring books)

They will not review any online submissions that do not include one of the above categories in the subject line. If they are interested, they will get back to you within 4-6 weeks. Unfortunately, due to the volume of queries, they will not be able to respond to everyone.

Small Beer Press

Gavin Grant
150 Pleasant Street
Suite 306
Easthampton, MA 01027
(413) 203-1636
info@lcrw.net
www.smallbeerpress.com/about/submission-guidelines

Creative Nonfiction, Essays, Story Collections, New Writers, Nonfiction

Small Beer Press publishes 6 to 10 books per year. They pay a small advance and standard royalties. Their e-book royalty rate is 40% of net receipts.

Send a query with a synopsis and the first 10 to 20 pages of the book (not the full manuscript) in standard manuscript format, and an SASE (with a Forever Stamp or an international reply coupon) by mail to the address above.

Small Publishers Association of North America
www.spannet.org

Master Stories, Writing Tips and Story Samples

This site helps publishers sell more books. Authors from small and independent presses may want to check this out.

Snowfall Press
www.snowfallpress.com/pricing

Printing Press

Snowfall Press is a printer, not a publisher, but you might want to know about this option if you decide to self-publish. As they are fond of saying, their customers print at the speed of life. That means that they have very few customers who print for a long term inventory strategy. They, in fact, encourage their publishers to only print what they sell, or certainly only what they are going to ship—today. To facilitate this, they don't force their customers to wait hours or even days to place an order. Orders can be placed as soon as books are uploaded. They always recommend printing proofs before placing any commercial orders.

Traditional prepress is expensive and takes valuable time. At Snowfall Press, they have automated this process so that as soon as a file is uploaded and an order is placed, the process takes minutes, without a person having to do anything.

Orders are printed in three days. Because they have built the Snowfall system to specifically work for print-to-order clients, the system is very fast. If their publishers order a book, or hundreds of books (same title or even different titles), their system is built to produce those books in three business days or less (not including the day of order). This could be an alternative to Amazon or IngramSpark, and their prices are competitive.

Soho Press

853 Broadway
New York, NY 10003
(212) 260-1900
soho@sohopress.com
www.sohopress.com/resources/submissions

YA Fiction, Novel, Literary Fiction, Thriller, Mystery, Crime

Soho Press is not currently accepting unagented, unsolicited submissions for their Crime or YA lists. When they complete moving to a new office, it is likely that they will be open to unsolicited submissions for their literary list. Familiarize yourself with the types of books they publish in the literary imprint "Soho Press" before submitting. In general, they are interested in bold voices and original ways of seeing the world.

Start by sending three chapters (or fifty pages) and a cover letter to Soho Press, care of the acquisitions editor. Accompany all submissions and queries with postage and packing materials for their return. It's not advised to send a query letter without sample pages—without seeing the actual writing, it's hard to get enthusiastic about a book.

Soho Press is not only the name of their press; it's the imprint within Soho dedicated to literary fiction (and the occasional memoir). The Soho Press imprint publishes bold literary voices—authors who craft new and powerful stories and offer readers fresh ways of seeing the world. Soho Press authors include Alex Shakar (*Luminarium*), Edwidge Danticat (*The Farming of Bones*), Matt Bell (*In the House Upon the Dirt Between the Lake and the Woods*), Paula Bomer (*Nine Months*), and dozens of other brilliant writers from across the globe.

Founded in 1986, Soho publishes 90 books a year across its Soho Press, Soho Crime and Soho Teen lists, and is known for introducing bold new literary voices, award-winning international crime fiction, and compelling young adult mystery and thrillers.

Sourcebooks
www.sourcebooks.com/resources/submissions-guidelines.html

Nonfiction, YA Fiction, Children's Books, Self-help, Memoirs, Creative Nonfiction

This publisher is not open to fiction submissions, but prospective authors may query them about children's, YA, and nonfiction. Their list includes most nonfiction categories, including memoir, history, college reference and study aids, entertainment, general self-help/psychology, business, parenting and special needs parenting, health and beauty, reference, education, biography, love and relationships, gift books and women's issues.

In order to consider your nonfiction book for potential publication, they need to see a proposal that includes the following items:

- A brief synopsis in 1-2 paragraphs
- Author bio or resume specifying credentials and publication credits, if any
- A complete table of contents, plus estimated length of manuscript in words and pages
- Two to three sample chapters (not the first)
- A description of the target audience
- One page/paragraph on your book's unique advantages
- A list of competing or comparable titles and how your book differs

Please e-mail queries to editorialsubmissions@sourcebooks.com.

Southern Yellow Pine Publishing

4351 Natural Bridge Rd.
Tallahassee, FL 32305
www.syppublishing.com/publish-your-book

New Writers, Nonfiction, Children's Books, Novel

At SYP Publishing they promote Southern authors of fiction and nonfiction. Southern Tales and Southern History are another important focus. SYP Publishing is dedicated to publishing texts on subjects of current or historical regional significance. They are interested in both fiction and nonfiction books.

The history and culture of the United States is rich and varied. There are many pieces of American culture, industry, lifestyle, and business that have not been fully recorded. They are committed to helping record those small pieces of the world that makes up the large tapestry of Americana. They love working with new and aspiring authors. They want to publish unique works set in specific locales that reflect the culture of that area. They want to help document the unusual, the lost art, the forgotten skill or the individuality of a special place.

They want to see characters brought to life that they can all love or hate. They also want to help local groups preserve their local history or topic of interest. They have the ability to publish small or large quantities. They publish in paperback, hardcover, and e-book formats.

Books can be submitted to their e-mail at tgerrell@syppublishing.com review. Please submit a short bio, a summary of who you think your reader is, and in what ways you are willing to help reach that reader and market.

Spokane Prize for Short Fiction

Christopher Howell
c/o Inland NW Center for Writers
668 N. Riverpoint Blvd.
2 RPT-#259
Spokane, WA 99202
www.willowspringsbooks.org/submit

New Writers, Story Collection, Literary Contest

Willow Springs Books invites submissions for the Spokane Prize for Short Fiction. The winner receives $2,000 plus publication. The contest is open to all United States authors, regardless of publication history.

To enter, submit a book-length manuscript. Manuscripts should be no less than 98 pages (with no maximum page count) and include at least 3 short stories. Manuscripts should be organized with page numbers and a table of contents. Stories may have been previously published in journals, anthologies, or limited edition volumes. However, selected story collections (stories previously published in books) will not be considered. Do not send novels. Please submit the following:

- an SASE for notification (if submission is by mail);
- a cover letter including your name, address, phone number, and e-mail address, as well as a short bio;
- and, lastly, a $27.50 reading fee paid through Submittable or via check made out to "Willow Springs Editions" (check or money order only) for each manuscript entry.

Spuyten Duyvil

spuyteneditors@gmail.com
www.spuytenduyvil.net/submissions.html

Poetry, New Writers, Nonfiction, Memoirs, Creative Nonfiction

This publisher embraces and encourages women, people of color, people with disabilities, LGBT writers, immigrants, internationals, and other writers who feel marginalized by mainstream madness.

This is a very small press, primarily a poetry press, centered in NYC. They do not publish fiction. "They are inspired by varied voices fractured in the current climate. Offering here, haven." They are open to those who've published many a book, and to those who've never published a book.

They look for work that is taut and raw, real as their own flesh quivering in the winter light. They thirst for work that breathes with an invisibly divine shudder when summer resurges once more. They are open to poetry and prose that is and makes new, and genre-bending cross-pollinating trans elocutions, too.

Stanford University Press
Kate Wahl
500 Broadway St.
Redwood City, CA 94063-3199
(650) 498-9420
kwahl@stanford.edu
www.sup.org/authors/editors

Nonfiction, Scholarly, International

Each editor at this press acquires books in certain specialty areas. Particular areas of interest include social, cultural, and political issues of interest to scholars, students, and the wider reading public. See the website above for particular editors' names and acquisition interests. They do not publish fiction.

Starving Artist Chapbooks

18390 SE Langensand
Sandy, OR 97055
www.cockcrowpress.com/starving.htm

Poetry, Chapbook

The Starving Artist Chapbook series, an imprint of Cockcrow Press, is designed to launch new voices in poetry into the literary atmosphere. The chapbooks are designed to be small in size (16 pages or less), yet grand in stature. They are open periodically for submissions.

When submissions are open, authors must submit manuscripts by mail to the address above. Time between acceptance and publication is 6 to 9 months. Authors can expect a small payment.

Steel Toe Books

Department of English
Western Kentucky University
1906 College Heights Blvd.
Suite 11086
Bowling Green, KY 42101-1086
www.steeltoebooks.submittable.com/submit

Poetry, Nonfiction, Literary Prize, Memoir, Hybrid

Steel Toe Books offers prizes for poetry, nonfiction, essays, story collections or novels. They have a $500 award and publication for a full length collection of prose in the form of Novel, Short Story, Essay, Creative Nonfiction, Memoir and hybrid forms. There is no maximum page count. All manuscripts are considered for standard publication. Longlist and shortlist announcements are made prior to the winner being selected. The winners of both contests will also receive a $1,000 promotional campaign across social media and other ad networks.

Those submitting will need to pay the $25 entry fee and submit the manuscript by September 1. The award winners receive $500 plus publication.

Steel Toe Books is affiliated with Western Kentucky University. Their authors have been featured on Garrison Keillor's radio program, "The Writer's Almanac," on Ted Kooser's newsletter, "American Life in Poetry," as well as on *Poetry Daily* and *Verse Daily*.

Steerforth Press
www.steerforth.com

Creative Nonfiction, Nonfiction

This press publishes high quality and beautifully designed books. Though Steerforth Press has published a range of titles on a variety of topics, they are currently focusing their acquisition energies on narrative nonfiction, such as investigative or literary journalism, true crime and history.

Steerforth Press is seeking projects that feature meticulous, original research and maintain a fidelity to the knowable facts while employing the novelist's tools of description, character development, dialogue and drama to tell stories that transport readers through time and space, that impart a deep emotional understanding of the personalities at play and the desires and challenges they faced as only enduring works of literature can do. True crime, political, military, cultural and sports histories, business narratives and exploration are among topics of potential interest.

Please send a query or proposal to submissions@steerforth.com. They do not accept unsolicited manuscript submissions.

Stephen F. Austin State University Press

c/o Dept of English
P.O. Box 13007
SFA Station
Nacogdoches, TX 75962-30007
(936) 468-1078
sfapress@sfasu.edu
www.sfasu.edu/sfapress/101.asp

New Writers, Hispanic, Novel, Story Collection, Poetry

Stephen F. Austin State University Press welcomes book proposals from both established and first-time writers. Great books are the lifeblood of any press, and Stephen F. Austin State University Press is dedicated to publishing well-written, well-researched books. They publish both academic and literary works.

They ask that you send a cover letter that includes a synopsis, the manuscript's length, the primary audience and any secondary audience(s) for the book, and similar books that your manuscript may compete with or complement.

They also want to see a biographical note and three sample chapters representative of the work (novel or short fiction) or 10 pages of poetry representative of the manuscript (poetry collections). Do not send the entire manuscript unless requested to do so. Direct proposals to "Acquisitions Editor" at: sfapress@sfasu.edu. You may also mail queries to the address above.

Stillhouse Press

www.stillhousepress.org/submissions

Poetry, Creative Nonfiction, Essays, Memoirs, Literary Fiction, Novel, Story Collection

Their goal is to publish a limited number of titles annually. They aim to produce well-made books, with an eye to the aesthetics of design, giving each project they select the careful attention required to make the publishing experience rewarding for the writer and the students and book professionals engaged in the process. They take time in considering all of their submissions and ask that you allow 3-6 months for a staff response.

All manuscripts should include a query letter, synopsis, and an overview of the work. Authors are also invited to share information about their writing background, online presence, involvement with the writing community, and inspiration for their work.

Only complete manuscripts of literary fiction (either a novel or a short story collection; no genre submissions), narrative nonfiction (a collection of linked essays or memoir), and poetry are accepted.

Their ideal manuscript is between 50,000 and 100,000 words of prose or 50-75 pages of poetry. All attachments should be in either PDF or Word DOC formats. They do not accept paper submissions.

www.stillhousepress.submittable.com/submit

Stone Bridge Press

1393 Solano Avenue
Suite C
Albany, CA 94706
sbpedit@stonebridge.com
www.stonebridge.com

Essays, Story Collection, Nonfiction, Novel, Literary Magazine

If you'd like to ask about the possibility of submitting a manuscript or idea to them, send a brief e-mail to the editor at the above address. The press is primarily focused on Japan, although other Asian interests are there, too.

StringTown Press
www.stringtownpress.org/faq

Fiction, Novel Excerpt, Poetry, Literary Magazine

Stringtown's literary magazine is taking submissions, but they are not currently taking unsolicited book manuscripts. They are a publisher based in the Northwest, and you'll have a better chance of getting published by them if you're an Oregon or Washington resident. That may open possibilities for book publication.

Poetry, fiction, creative nonfiction, novel excerpts or a form all your own are acceptable. Submissions containing one story or one essay or three to five poems is generally appropriate. They are also open to art work, but keep in mind they have a minuscule budget.

www.stringtownpress.submittable.com/submit

Sunbury Press

www.sunburypress.submittable.com/submit

New Writers, Fantasy, Nonfiction, Essays, Crime, Historical Fiction, Novel, Thriller, Steampunk

This publisher is looking for historical, mystery/thriller, police procedural, detective, legal, horror, fantasy, science, literary, romance, steampunk, urban, dystopian, metaphysical and visionary fiction. They only accept about 7 percent of submitted manuscripts.

The publisher's other imprints focus on history, memoir, true crime, science, self-help, sports, reference, paranormal, nature, pets, philosophy, legal, business, art, nutrition, longevity, elder care, biography or autobiography.

As far as Young Adult categories, they will consider historical, mystery/thriller, detective, fantasy, science, literary, romance, steampunk, urban, dystopian, metaphysical, visionary, history, memoir, true crime, science, self-help, sports, reference, paranormal, pets, biography or autobiography.

Fill out the form on the Submittable website above to get started with the process. They only choose books that they feel will succeed in the marketplace.

Sunstone Press

Submissions Editor
P.O. Box 2321
Santa Fe, NM, 87504-2321
www.sunstonepress.com/about.html

Story Collection, Novel, Fiction, New Writers, Children's

Sunstone Press has been an independent publisher since 1971, and is located in downtown Santa Fe, New Mexico. Its books are sold nationally and internationally.

To submit, send the following:

- an author bio;
- a sample chapter;
- a table of contents;
- a statement about why Sunstone Press should publish the book;
- a preliminary marketing plan;
- and an SASE.

The publisher does not accept e-mails or electronic submissions.

All their fiction has to do with Native-American themes. This includes their mysteries. They have many activity books and children's books.

Syracuse University Press

Mary Selden Evans
621 Skytop Road
Suite 110
Syracuse, NY 13244-5290
www.syracuseuniversitypress.syr.edu/guidelines.html

Nonfiction, Poetry, Novels

Authors wishing to propose a new book project, should complete a New Book Proposal Form (PDF) and e-mail to the appropriate acquisitions editor, along with a current curriculum vitae and a preliminary table of contents. Note that the press does not accept unsolicited manuscripts or unrevised dissertations. They are not currently considering memoirs, and consider fiction and poetry only very selectively.

If the acquisitions editor—often in cooperation with a series editor—determines that your project is an appropriate fit for their list, you may be invited to submit a complete manuscript for confidential external peer review. Your manuscript will be sent to two expert readers simultaneously for evaluation.

Once they agree to begin the peer review process, they will only review the manuscript on an exclusive basis. Please note that the peer review process can take several months, according to the availability and schedules of external readers. See their guidelines for additional information on the interests of specific editors.

Tailwinds Press

P.O. Box 2283
Radio City Station
New York, NY 10101-2283.
submissions@tailwindspress.com
www.tailwindspress.com/contact-us.html

Essays, Creative Nonfiction, Memoirs, Nonfiction, Literary Fiction

Tailwinds Press is a young, New York City-based independent press specializing in high-quality literary fiction and nonfiction. Tailwinds Press is edited by dedicated individuals with significant experience in writing, print media, academia, and project execution. They believe in intelligent work that is compelling and relevant to the spirit of our times.

A tailwind is a wind that blows in the direction of travel of an object, increasing the object's speed and reducing the time required to reach its destination. Tailwinds are generally considered to be beneficial to pilots, runners, and cyclists.

They publish four to six books a year, and they do not publish genre fiction.

TAMU Press

Lewis Street
4354 TAMU
College Station, TX 77843-4354
www.tamupress.com/pages/editorial_program.aspx

Nonfiction

Like most university presses, TAMU Press publishes nonfiction exclusively. Subject areas that A&M Press publishes include:

- Agriculture and Range Ecology
- Anthropology, Physical
- Aviation History and History of Space Flight
- Borderlands Studies
- Business and Oil History
- Gardening and Horticulture
- Historical Archaeology (Texas and the Southwest)
- Military History
- Natural History
- Nature and the Environment
- Nautical Archaeology
- Political Communication
- Presidential Studies
- Regional History (Texas, Western, Southern, Southwestern)
- Texas Arts and Humanities
- Veterinary Medicine
- Wildlife Science

For other topics, inquiries may be addressed to the editors at emilyseyl@exchange.tamu.edu. Subject areas that A&M Press does not publish include poetry, memoirs or genealogy, fiction, kids' books, and cookbooks.

Tanstaafl Press

submissions@tanstaaflpress.com
www.tanstaaflpress.com/submission-guidelines/

Fantasy, Novel, Sci fi

Tanstaafl Press is looking for prolific sci fi writers who can get out on the road and speak. The Press publishes only fiction. They focus on science fiction, cyberpunk, alternative histories, post apocalyptic and fantasy of novel length. They will consider exceptional works from other genres of fiction or short story compilations from their main areas of interest.

All submissions must be sent as single e-mails to the editors at submissions@tanstaaflpress.com. All attachments must contain the submission title, the author's name, the author's contact information (e-mail as minimum). All e-mails should contain a cover letter describing your writing history, what you are intending to accomplish with your work, and what you want out of a publisher. Submissions must contain a text document containing approximately the first 1000 words of your work.

Any work that starts with a dream sequence or has a dream sequence as a major plot point will be rejected with no response. Submissions must contain a 300-500 word summary of your work.

TANSTAAFL Press accepts submissions that are sent at the same time to other publishers.

Tarpaulin Sky

P.O. Box 189
Grafton, VT 05146
www.tarpaulinsky.com/

Nonfiction, Memoirs, Literary Fiction, Story Collection, Poetry, Fiction, New Writers

Tarpaulin Sky is a micro-press that publishing literary writing in both book form, online, and in their affiliated magazine. They have an annual reading period that selects two manuscripts for full book publication. Sign up for their newsletter to learn about open submission periods.

If time and resources permit, TS editors may choose additional manuscripts for publication. Unpublished individual works (or excerpts) from manuscript submissions may be considered for publication in their literary magazine.

Follow them on Facebook to learn when they're next reading for their book awards.

www.facebook.com/tarpaulinskypress

TCU Press
www.prs.tcu.edu/author-guidelines.asp

Nonfiction, Novel

TCU Press publishes original regional literary fiction but does not consider genre fiction nor manuscripts that are clearly suited to a commercial publishing house. TCU Press reprints classic Texas novels in its Texas Tradition Series.

E-mail query letters and/or proposals to the Press at tcupress@tcu.edu. Nonfiction proposals should include a letter describing the project, a table of contents, introduction, and sample. For fiction, please send a plot synopsis and a short sample.

Simultaneous submissions are not encouraged. The press sends out prospectuses to professional readers, and the editors aim to send these prospectuses blind. Therefore, please do not put your name on every page of the prospectus or manuscript. Listing your name on the title page is sufficient.

Telling Their Stories

185 AJK Blvd.
Suite 246
Lewisburg, PA 17837
info@TellingOurStoriesPress.com
www.tellingourstoriespress.com/guidelines

Anthology, New Writers, Memoirs, Creative Nonfiction

They've published several anthologies with short pieces of memoirs and essays. They don't publish whole books, but this is a place to submit shorter personal essays and memoirs. They're very open to work submitted by new writers.

Texas Review Press

P.O. Box 2146
Huntsville, TX 77341
(936) 294-1992
www.texasreviewpress.org/submissions

Fiction, Nonfiction, Poetry

Texas Review Press publishes poetry, fiction, nonfiction, and scholarly works. Topics they are interested in include 20th/21st Century American Poetry, Environmental Writing, Ecopoetics, Contemporary Poetics, Creative Writing Pedagogy, Southern Literature, Southern Issues, Gulf of Mexico Studies, Texas/Louisiana Literature, Texas/Louisiana History, Folklore, Cajun-Creole Studies, African-American Literature, African-American Studies, Latinx Literature, Latinx Studies, & Texas/Mexico History.

Poetry Proposals should include a title, cover letter, a short author biography, a curriculum vitae, and a sample of 10 poems from the manuscript. If interested, the editors will request the entire manuscript.

Fiction and nonfiction proposals should include a title, cover letter, table of contents, summary of the project, two sample chapters/stories, an estimated word count, a short author biography, and a curriculum vitae. If interested, the editors will request the entire manuscript.

Scholarly works' proposals should include a title, cover letter, abstract, two sample chapters, an estimated word count, a short author biography, and a curriculum vitae. They are not interested in unrevised dissertations; dissertations should be revised for a general audience and formatted in accordance with the Chicago Manual of Style. If interested, the editors will request the entire manuscript.

If TRP is interested in pursuing your project, it will move on to the peer-review and editorial processes.

Texas Tech University Press

2903 4th St.
P.O. Box 41037
Lubbock, TX 79409-1037
www.ttup.ttu.edu/about.html

Hispanic, YA Fiction, Children's Books, Military, Memoirs, Nonfiction, Novel

Texas Tech University Press, in business since 1971, is currently signing nonfiction titles in natural history and the natural sciences; eighteenth-century and Joseph Conrad studies; studies of modern Southeast Asia, particularly the Vietnam War; costume and textile history; and all subject areas relating to Texas, the Great Plains, and the American West, especially biography, history, memoir, and travel.

In addition, the press signs one invited poetry manuscript annually and occasionally a regional novel with national appeal. You may wish to contact them here: www.ttup.ttu.edu/contact.html. Ask for a current Press catalog to review their list.

Although all titles must pass a rigorous review in terms of substance, many of their published titles address or embrace a general readership. To submit a book proposal to them, send a two- to four-page typed outline or annotated contents, indicating the nature and scope of each chapter and any significant appendixes. Your proposal should also include an introduction, a minimum of two sample chapters, and a cover letter with the following:

- title and anticipated manuscript length, as well as number and kind of graphic materials, if any;
- your description of (and estimate of) the size of the audience toward which you are directing the book;
- a comparison of your book to others published on the subject and why your treatment of the subject is unique;
- and, a brief autobiographical summary about why you are qualified to write this book and the nature and scope of your research.

Make sure you list your complete address (including e-mail, if any), with a daytime phone number. Send an SASE with adequate postage.

The Ashland Poetry Press

Ashland University
Bixler Center for the Humanities
401 College Avenue
Ashland, OH 44805
(419) 289-5098
www.app.ashland.edu
www.ashlandpoetrypress.com

Literary Contest, Poetry, Translation

Ashland Poetry Press seeks to publish and promote the best poetry submitted from new and established authors writing in English, as well as translations of Spanish poetry into English.

Their annual Richard Snyder Poetry Prize results in publication, plus $1000. The submission fee is $27, and the manuscripts must be 48 to 96 pages. The submission deadline is May 1.

www.ashlandpoetrypress.submittable.com/submit

The Backwaters Prize

3502 North 52nd Street
Omaha, NE 68104-3506
(402) 451-4052
www.thebackwaterspress.com

Literary Contest, Poetry

The submission period for the Backwaters Prize ends on May 31. The prize is a $2,500.00 cash prize plus publication of your book in trade paperback, plus 30 copies of the book to the poet.

Submit full-length manuscripts of original poetry in English, between 60 to 85 typewritten pages (not including credits, title page, and contents' page) in an easily legible font, such as Times New Roman or Garamond, in either 11- or 12-point type.

www.universityofnebraskapress.submittable.com/submit

The Feminist Press

Submissions Committee
365 Fifth Avenue
Suite 5406
New York, NY 10016
www.feministpress.org/submissions

Women, Story Collection, Nonfiction, Novel, Memoirs

Take a look at their catalog, website, and mission statement to see if your work would in any way fit into their publishing program. (Note, they do not publish poetry, drama, doctoral dissertations, or literary criticism.)

Be sure to include a synopsis of your work, three sample chapters, a short author bio, and a brief marketing plan, along with any relevant contact information in order to receive a reply to your submission. If you do not have an e-mail address, include an SASE with your submission. Note that they cannot return any of your materials; they will send you a reply letter in that SASE.

They also accept digital submissions. You can e-mail your proposal as a PDF to editor@feministpress.org.

They appreciate your patience in awaiting a reply. Their small staff receives hundreds of submissions each season, and they publish only fifteen to twenty books a year.

The Clay Reynolds Novella Prize
Texas Review Press
P.O. Box 2146
Huntsville, TX 77341
(936) 294-1992

New Writers, Novella, Literary Contest

The Clay Reynolds Novella Prize is sponsored by Texas Review Press. Novellas can be between 20,000 and 50,000 words. Submissions are open January 1—March 31, and the winner will be announced in March. Winners receive a $500 prize, a standard royalty contract from Texas Review Press, and 20 copies of the published book.

Simultaneous submissions are acceptable. Please notify TRP immediately by withdrawing the manuscript via Submittable if the manuscript is accepted elsewhere. Details about formatting requirements can be found on TRP's Submittable page.

www.texasreview.submittable.com/submit/1488/the-clay-reynolds-novella-prize

The Kelpies Prize

15 Harrison Gardens
Edinburgh, Scotland
United Kingdom EH11 1SH
0131-337 2372
www.florisbooks.co.uk/kelpiesprize/

Scotland, Children's Books, Literary Contest, Fiction

If you are Scottish and write children's books, then this prize is a good one. To submit to the Kelpies Prize, send the first five chapters of a book for children, plus a synopsis (2-3 paragraphs) summarizing the whole book, so the judges can see how the story will develop.

They also require a short piece of writing (1,000-3,000 words) for children that begins with:

[Character name] had a secret that no one must ever discover...

February 28 is their annual deadline. The starting sentence changes on a yearly basis.

www.discoverkelpies.co.uk/kelpies-prizes/kelpies-prize-writing/enter/

The Parliament House

www.parliamenthousepress.com/submissions

Fantasy, Steampunk, Sci fi

The Parliament House curates fantasy of every sort. Be it contemporary, steampunk, paranormal, urban, or otherwise, it has to be the sort of magic that captures their attention and leaves a lasting impression.

When it comes to new prospects, the Parliament House has a sharp and discerning taste. They specialize in fantasy, be it paranormal, contemporary, urban, or otherwise. Your characters must be unique, and your voice must capture their attention. They are looking for the different and unusual, not another *Twilight* or *Harry Potter* retelling (though classic fairy tale retellings are acceptable, as long as they have a fresh twist).

At The Parliament House, they're proud to offer some of the highest royalties in the industry. Digital-first releases receive up to 35% of cover price, while print royalties receive 7.5% of cover price. Currently, Parliament House releases titles in digital-first format, and upon a successful digital run, will then release the book in print and audio. Manuscripts should be 50,000 to 140,000 words.

The Permanent Press

Judith Shepard
4170 Noyac Road
Sag Harbor, NY 11963
www.thepermanentpress.com/index.php/submissions.html

Memoirs, Novel, Literary Fiction

"On a shoestring, turning out literary gems."— *The New York Times*

Here's what they publish...Their interest is in discovering novelists who have the talent to write exceptional fiction. They do not accept electronic submissions. If you would like to be considered, you must mail a hard copy to the address above.

Only submit a sample of approximately the first 25 pages. If they are interested, they will request the entire manuscript.

If you have any questions contact them at:

info@thepermanentpress.com.

The Tuscarora Award

Brittany Loefler
Asst. Fiction Editor
P.O. Box 63927
Philadelphia, PA 19147
(610) 764-0813
hiddenriverarts@gmail.com
www.hiddenriverartssubmissions.submittable.com/submit

Historical Fiction, Novel

Hidden River offers the Tuscarora Award for an unpublished, book-length work of historical fiction. The winning manuscript will be published by Hidden River Press, an imprint of Hidden River Publishing, and will receive $1000 plus ten copies of the book. The entry fee is $22. This competition is open to international submissions for all writers in English.

Be aware that they consider all forms of publication as disqualification. Self-publishing is publication; if your manuscript has an isbn number, or if it is available for sale online and/or in brick and mortar stores, your book is "published".

All submissions must include name, address, telephone number, e-mail, website (if you have one), a brief biography, outline, full synopsis and full manuscript. Online submissions are strongly encouraged. Note that, when submitting online, all materials must be combined into one document before uploading. Be sure to upload all required materials, including the synopsis before the manuscript, which should be uploaded last.

Simultaneous submissions are accepted. They ask only that you contact them asap if you place the manuscript for publication elsewhere.

Notice that Hidden River Arts has several other publication opportunities, including for novels, plays, and YA fiction.

The University of Arizona Press

Kathryn Conrad
355 S. Euclid Ave.
Suite 103
Tucson, AZ 85719
www.uapress.arizona.edu/authors/proposalguidelines

Hispanic, Nonfiction, Memoirs, LatinX

The University of Arizona Press, founded in 1959 as a department of the University of Arizona, is a nonprofit publisher of scholarly and regional books. As a delegate of the University of Arizona to the larger world, the Press publishes the work of scholars wherever they may be, concentrating upon scholarship that reflects the special strengths of the University of Arizona, Arizona State University, and Northern Arizona University.

The University of Arizona Press publishes about fifty-five books annually and has more than 1,000 books in print. These include scholarly titles in Native studies, anthropology, archaeology, environmental studies, geography, Chicano studies, history, Latin American studies, and the space sciences.

The UA Press also publishes general interest books on Arizona and the Southwest borderlands. In addition, the Press publishes two series in literature: Sun Tracks: An American Indian Literary Series and Camino del Sol: A Chicana/o Literary Series.

Many UA Press books have been translated into foreign languages including Chinese, French, German, Italian, Japanese, and Spanish. UA Press books are printed by commercial printers, typically located out of state, which specialize in producing short-run books. All UA Press books are printed on acid-free, archival quality paper. Read their guidelines for information on submissions.

The University of Michigan Press
Sweetwater Fiction Series
Fiction Editor
The University of Michigan Press
 839 Greene Street
Ann Arbor, MI 48104-3209
ump.fiction@umich.edu
www.press.umich.edu/series.do?id=UM141

Fiction, Novella, Novel

In addition to their annual Michigan Literary Fiction Awards (see the link above), The University of Michigan Press also publishes literary fiction linked to the Great Lakes region. Such fiction is part of their Sweetwater Fiction series. They welcome both new and established authors. They have no restrictions as to style or subject matter, but are unlikely to consider genre fiction, such as mystery, religious, science fiction, romance, and children's fiction.

To ensure that your work receives proper attention, they ask that you submit via regular mail. Send a cover letter and a sample consisting of approximately the first thirty pages (or two stories) of the manuscript. Provided that your work meets the above requirements, there is no need to query in advance. Work submitted without an SASE will not receive a response.

Send materials to the address above. Due to new USPS safety regulations requiring that packages over 16 oz. be hand delivered directly to a post office worker, they are unable to return manuscripts, even with an SASE.

The University of South Carolina Press

1600 Hampton Street
5th Floor
Columbia, SC 29208
www.sc.edu/uscpress/submission.html

Nonfiction

The University of South Carolina Press publishes works of original scholarship in the fields of history (American, African-American, Southern, Civil War, culinary, maritime, and women's), regional studies, literature, religious studies, and rhetoric. USC Press also publishes regional general interest titles addressing the art, architecture, culture, fiction, gardening, and outdoors of the American South.

They will accept submissions only via e-mail; they do not accept paper submissions. Submissions in the fields of Southern history, African-American studies, and civil rights should be sent to Ehren Foley, PhD: foleyek@e-mail.sc.edu; those involving literary studies, rhetoric and communications, and regional interest should be sent to Aurora Bell: aurorab@mailbox.sc.edu. If you are not sure whether your project is an appropriate fit for the Press, send a brief e-mail inquiry to the editor whose remit best aligns with your book. Please allow four to six weeks for the Press to respond to your proposal.

The University of Utah Press

J. Willard Marriott Library
Suite 5400
University of Utah
295 South 1500 East
Salt Lake City, UT 84112-0860
(801) 585-9786
www.uofupress.com/authors.php

Poetry, Nonfiction, Literary Prize, Environmental, Creative Nonfiction

The University of Utah Press is an agency of the J. Willard Marriott Library of the University of Utah. In accordance with the mission of the University, the Press publishes and disseminates scholarly books in selected fields, as well as other printed and recorded materials of significance to Utah, the region, the country, and the world. They have some incredible prizes for environmental writing, poetry, etc.

The University of Utah Press is delighted to consider your book for publication. They will do their best to carry it through the publishing process as expeditiously as possible. They aim to produce an attractive, high-quality book, and to do this, they need your help.

Send a description of the book, a marketing plan, the number of pages and illustrations, a preface, and sample chapter.

The Waywiser Press

P.O. Box 6205
Baltimore, MD 21206
www.waywiser-press.com

British, Fiction, Novel, Poetry, Literary Prize

The Waywiser Press is a small, independent company with its main office in the U.K. and a subsidiary in the U.S. It was founded in late 2001 and started publishing in 2002.

Waywiser is a literary press, first and foremost, with a special interest in modern poetry and fiction. From time to time, however, they also issue books belonging to other literary genres—e.g. memoir, criticism, and history. They are keen to promote the work of new, as well as established authors, and would like to rescue still others from undeserved neglect.

Prose authors may submit a manuscript at any time of the year. The press will endeavor to respond within 3-4 months. Authors should not send complete manuscripts in the first instance. Instead, they should send a synopsis of not more than 500 words as well as two chapters.

Together with the synopsis and chapters, you should send a resumé or c.v. Amongst other things, this should list any previous publications. All submissions should be sent to their U.K. office (see below).

The Waywiser Press (Submissions)
Christmas Cottage, Church Enstone
Chipping Norton, Oxfordshire
United Kingdom, OX7 4NN

If return of a rejected manuscript is required, or you wish to be informed of their decision by post, your submission should be accompanied by a stamped self-addressed envelope. Note that if the stamps or international reply coupons (IRCs) supplied are insufficient for the purpose, the press reserves the right to dispose of manuscript material without further notice.

Poetry can be submitted through the Anthony Hecht Poetry Prize during their contest reading period. Authors with two or more previous collections of poetry may submit a manuscript between March 1st and July 1st in any particular year. The press will endeavor to respond by the end of October.

Three Rooms Press

submissions@threerooms.com
www.threeroomspress.com/submit

Fiction, New Writers, Mystery, Sci fi, Nonfiction, Novel, YA

Here's what they want in fiction. Think contemporary. Urban. Satire. Absurd. Historical that astonishes. Think detective/crime/gangster with a modern twist. Think humor and heart. Think powerful. Think interesting. Think utterly compelling and unique. At present, they are particularly interested in gutty, New York-based contemporary fiction; mystery fiction with strong female protagonists; cyberpunk/technopian-themed novels.

For details of what to send, see the website above or e-mail submissions@threeroomspress.com.

Tilbury House

Jonathan Eaton
www.tilburyhouse.com/submissions

Children's Books, Nonfiction

A regional publisher in Maine, Tilbury House narrowed its editorial focus several years ago. Their primary emphasis is on nonfiction picture books that appeal to children (ages 5—10) and their parents. They want these books to offer solid learning content and strong appeal for bookstores.

They are always interested in picture books that explore cultural diversity and nature and the environment, and they are also looking for history, biography, and science and engineering picture books. Good picture books enrich children's education and cultivate their imaginations, creativity, and critical thinking.

Other tips/suggestions:

- primary picture book text (approx. 500 to 800 words) for children ages 3 to 5;
- nonfiction texts for juvenile picture books 5 and up—school curriculum related;
- nonfiction texts for older readers 8 and up—school curriculum related;
- and nonfiction manuscripts for Young Adult Readers 12 and up.

They will also consider nonfiction chapter books and graphic nonfiction for early readers (ages 8—13) and nonfiction for young adult readers (YA, age 12+).

They rarely publish fables, fantasies, picture books with talking animals, or other fictions.

Tilbury House will also consider submissions for adult reference/how-to (i.e., gardening, home improvement, etc.) and nautical titles (reference/how-to) that have national appeal.

Toad Press

www.toadpress.blogspot.com/p/submission-information.html

Translation, Chapbook, Translation

Toad Press accepts open submissions of chapbook-length translations for its International Chapbook Series each year between October 15 and December 31. They publish one to three chapbooks a year and accept online submissions only. Send approximately 14-26 pages of poetry or prose, a cover sheet with name and contact information, a table of contents (if applicable), and acknowledgments' page via their Submittable page.

www.toadpress.submittable.com/Submit

There is no reading fee, but they do think it's pretty super when you purchase one of their previously published chapbooks when you submit your manuscript.

Simultaneous submissions are encouraged, but do them the courtesy of withdrawing your manuscript immediately if it is accepted elsewhere.

Did you remember that they only publish translations? Great!

Questions? Take a look at their Frequently Asked Questions. If that doesn't help, e-mail them at toadpress@hotmail.com.

Tolson Books
www.tolsunbooks.com

Poetry, Short Stories, Essays, Literary Fiction, New Writers

Tolsun Books accepts full-length manuscripts made from pieces: poetry, short stories, flash memoir, essays, comics, poetry, photo-essays, translations, hybrids, and things they've never seen before. They do not accept novels, full-length memoirs, or genre fiction (romance, horror, thrillers).

They value voice, energy, and inclusiveness. They have published many first-time authors, as well as experienced writers. They love potential, and they are willing to work through manuscripts that might not yet be polished. Watch their Submittable page for the next open submissions' period.

www.firstimpressions.submittable.com/submit

They are a very small company, and submission fees help them print and distribute books, pay royalties and licensing fees, and market their catalog. Their motto is "reverse gentrification of the literary world."

Tor Books

Tom Doherty Associates, LLC
175 Fifth Avenue
New York, NY 10010
www.us.macmillan.com/torforge/about/faq#how-do-i-submit-writing-to-tom-doherty-associates-llc

New Writers, Novella, Sci fi, Novel

Tor Books wants to see the actual writing, not a query. For writers who don't have agents, send the first three chapters of the book, prepared in standard manuscript format on white paper. (If the chapters are very short or really long, or you don't use chapter breaks, send the first 40-60 pages of the book, up to a maximum of 10,000 words.) The submitted text must be made up of consecutive pages and should end at the end of a paragraph, not in mid-sentence. Tor Books publishes exclusively science fiction.

Standard manuscript format means margins of at least 1 inch all the way around; indented paragraphs; double-spaced text; and Times New Roman in 12-point type. Use one side of the page only. Do not justify the text. Do not bind the manuscript in any way. Make sure the header of the manuscript includes the author's name and/or the title of the book as well as the page number (on every page).

Include a synopsis of the entire book. The synopsis should include all important plot elements, especially the end of the story, as well as character development for the main characters. The synopsis should run between three and ten pages in standard manuscript format. The first page of the synopsis and the first page of the text should also include the author's name and contact information and the title of the manuscript.

Include a dated cover letter that includes your name and contact information and the title of the submitted work. Briefly tell them what genre or subgenre the submission falls into and mention any qualifications you have that pertain to the work. List any previous publications in paying markets.

Include a self-addressed, stamped, business-size envelope for their reply letter. They understand that writers living outside the United States may not be able to supply International Reply Coupons. You may submit regardless; send a self-addressed, business-size envelope for their reply.

They recycle all proposals in accordance with corporate sustainability directives and local laws. If you do not include an SASE, you will not receive a reply.

Send only one proposal in each submissions' packet. If you have written a series, send a proposal for the first book only. If they like what they see, they'll ask for the rest.

Many people include postcards to be returned when the proposal reaches them. Unfortunately, they don't open submissions until they're ready to read them, so it's probably best to save your money.

Address submissions as follows:

- Science fiction and fantasy: Acquisitions Editor, Science Fiction and Fantasy
- Fiction of all other types including but not limited to general fiction, historical fiction, horror, mystery, paranormal, suspense/thriller, urban fantasy, and women's fiction: Acquisitions Editor, Fiction
- Children's and Young Adult: Acquisitions Editor, Children's and Young Adult Division

They only publish books for the chapter book, middle grade, and young adult audiences. They do not publish picture books.

If you do not receive a reply after six months, resubmit. It's likely that your project or their response disappeared in transit.

Torrey House Press

2806 E. Melony Drive
Salt Lake City, UT 84124
mail@torreyhouse.com
www.torreyhouse.org/submissions

Novel, Story Collection, Essays, Creative Nonfiction, Environmental

Torrey House Press publishes 8-10 books per year of literary novels, full-length short story collections, essay collections, creative nonfiction, and the occasional anthology. They are interested in well-crafted work with environmental, natural history, or natural landscape themes, and writing which explores the value of well-managed public lands and the transformative power of wilderness. THP does not currently accept submissions for poetry or books for children. They accept agented and unagented work.

In an effort to be green and organized, they ask that authors submit manuscripts electronically through the submission manager link below. Keep in mind that the most successful submission will articulate why you and your work are a good fit for Torrey House Press. Tell them how you found them in your cover letter.

www.torreyhousepress.submittable.com/submit

For fiction, include a synopsis, some background on yourself, who your readership is, and how you propose to market your work. Submit your entire manuscript along with your cover letter.

For nonfiction manuscripts, including memoirs or essay collections, send a query first. Submit a one or two page overview of your book idea along with information about yourself, why you are qualified to write on the subject, who your audience is, and how you propose to market your work.

If they like what they see, they will request a full proposal. For a full proposal, once requested, include a cover letter, a resume, a preliminary table of contents, a one or two-paragraph summary of each chapter, a list of other books on the topic, details and specifics of your target audience, a summary of any market research, and any completed chapters.

TouchWood Editions

103-1075 Pendergast Street
Victoria, BC
Canada V8V 0A1
submissions@touchwoodeditions.com
www.touchwoodeditions.com

Literary Fiction, Memoir, Nonfiction, Creative Nonfiction, Canadian

TouchWood Editions only publishes Canadian authors, with a strong preference for authors from, and who write about topics pertinent to Western Canada (includes BC, AB, SK, MB and the North).

At TouchWood, we are committed to doing our part in correcting the historical and societal imbalance of representation in literature. In the spirit of moving towards an inclusive publishing program that reflects the rich diversity of our communities, we welcome submissions from Indigenous writers, writers of colour, writers with disabilities, writers from the LGBTQIA2S community, and writers from any other community that have historically been underrepresented. If you identify with any of these communities, and you feel comfortable in doing so, we encourage you to mention this in your submission letter.

www.touchwoodeditions.com/submit-a-manuscript/

In your e-mail, please include a brief summary of what your book is about and how you feel it will fit with our publishing program. Make sure to include your e-mail address and phone number. Attach your book proposal in a single PDF document. Do not send multiple attachments. Your book proposal should include:

- a synopsis of the work
- a marketing plan and info about your current platform
- a biography, including your publication history
- sample chapters and a table of contents
- sample images
- contact information
- any other pertinent information that will help us understand how we can successfully collaborate with you on your project

If we would like to see more, we'll get in touch.

Tramp Press (Irish)

submissions@tramppress.com
www.tramppress.com/submissions

Story Collection, Novel, Literary Fiction

Tramp Press is always looking for exceptional new works of fiction. If you're an exceptional writer, they're looking for you. To submit your work, send the following to them at submissions@tramppress.com.

They'd like to see a good-sized sample of your work (fiction only).

They aren't currently accepting any poetry or nonfiction such as memoirs or histories). Send a few chapters (they do not have to be sequential—they want you to wow them, and if the big wow happens in Chapter 4, then by all means send that on to them), or a few short stories. If you don't have chapters or your short stories vary a lot in length, a good rule of thumb is that they'd like to read roughly 50 pages or 10,000 words.

In your cover letter, tell them a little bit about yourself, your writing experience and your influences. They love to hear about why you think your work would be a good match.

A synopsis would be fine—three pages, also fine. They'd like to hear the full story from beginning to end, so don't hold back on spoilers!

If you're a person of colour, they're particularly looking for you. If you identify in any way with a group that has been under-represented in literature, they're looking for you.

In fact, all you need to be published by Tramp Press is 1) be an exceptional writer! And 2) follow the submission guidelines.

They have an open submissions policy, which means you can submit whenever you like—you don't have to e-mail them first to ask. Just fire away as per the instructions below. You don't have to be Irish—in fact you don't have to be anything at all, except great at writing.

Now for the bad news. Unfortunately, it's very likely that they won't publish your work. Like most presses, they turn down the vast majority of submissions sent to them by writers and agents, and with just a couple of new books a year, they are ridiculously picky. They publish three books a year, after reading through about a thousand manuscripts first.

Transmundane Press

www.transmundanepress.com/submissions.html

Novella, Novel, Fantasy, Horror

Transmundane Press publishes fantasy and scary fiction. They release e-book and print formats. At a minimum, books should be 35,000 words in length, although they prefer 60-80,000 words; however, longer works are also considered. Do note that shorter works are considered for anthologies and works less than 50,000 words will be published in e-book format only.

In general, they look for crisp dialogue, believable characters, interesting premises, and fast-paced action. Entertain and educate. Readers like to learn while they're being entertained, so don't be afraid to teach your readers something.

Technical skill is key. If too many errors exist in the first few pages, the manuscript will be sent back. They polish your books, not correct errors that the author should have fixed in the first place.

They do not publish anything with pedophilia, which involves sexual situations between adults and children. They are not interested in "barely legal" situations either. They are really not interested in reading about rape or incest. They do not accept fan fiction because it may have issues with copyright infringement.

They pay competitive royalties. For details about what you should send them, read their submissions' guidelines.

Travelers' Tales

Larrry Habegger
853 Alma Street
Palo Alto, CA 94301
www.travelerstales.com

Anthology, Travel, Nonfiction, Creative Nonfiction, Essays, Literary Contest

Nonfiction travel stories for either their anthologies or for e-book distribution should be submitted through their Gateway program. Manuscripts will be considered for e-book publication and also for release in print.

Please submit your book-length, nonfiction manuscript after completing the contact information. Please note that this link is not for individual stories. Travelers' Tales/Solas House does not guarantee publication of any manuscript received, nor does your submission prevent you from submitting to other publishers.

We will review your manuscript as soon as we can to see if there is a good fit with our program. Unfortunately, due to the volume of submissions, we will only respond if we have an interest in publishing your book.

www.travelerstalesstories.com/author_info.cfm

This publisher also sponsors the Solas Awards for best travel stories. The winner receives $1000 and publication. There are also $750 and $500 awards for runners up.

Turtle Point Press

208 Java Street, 5th Floor
Brooklyn, NY 11222
(212) 741-1393
info@turtlepointpress.com
www.turtlepointpress.com

Memoirs, Literary Fiction, Poetry, Novel

Turtle Point Press is an independent publisher distinguished by books of superior literary content and elegant design. The Press has been delighting readers with new fiction, literary nonfiction, poetry, memoirs, works in translation, and rediscovered classics since 1990.

On the horizon, future titles will introduce more women writers and West Coast writers, and broaden the largely French international line to literary fiction and nonfiction that spans the globe.

When they reopen for submissions, query with a brief project description and author bio. They will respond if they wish to see sample material.

Twisted Road Publications

1400 Village Square Blvd.
Suite 3-234
Tallahassee, FL 32312
www.twistedroadpublications.com

New Writers, Novel, Fiction

Many of today's talented writers have encountered impossible barriers blocking the road to publication. Corporate hierarchies, with their marketing directors and entrenched practices of exclusiveness, are convinced they know what readers want. With the resurgence of small presses, some of those barriers are being taken down. Still, the journey of a story from concept to finished book in the hands of an adoring reader often takes a very twisted road. TRP seeks to publish gifted writers whose works are under-represented by corporate marketing.

They are partial to the writer who possesses a gift for compassionate, sharp-eyed truth-telling, rendering fully formed characters and stories that get under their skin. Ones that push hard to discover the kind of truth that exposes the reality of their deepest humanity.

Their selection process, simply stated, is: If they're blown away by the quality of the work and its intent isn't racist, homophobic, elitist, sexist or erotic for the sake of erotica—although they like sex and welcome its inclusion—then you are well on your way with them. If they want to publish your work, they'll make you an offer. If it is an offer you choose not to accept, they're cool with that.

www.twistedroadpublications.com/submissions/

Two Dollar Radio

1124 Parsons Ave.
Columbus, OH 43206
www.twodollarradio.com

Literary Fiction, Memoirs, Novel, Nonfiction

Two Dollar Radio is a family-run outfit founded in 2005 with the mission to reaffirm the cultural and artistic spirit of the publishing industry. They aim to do this by presenting bold works of literary merit, each book, individually and collectively, providing a sonic progression that they believe to be too loud to ignore.

Our books and films aren't for everyone. The last thing the world needs is an indie press releasing books that could just as easily carry a corporate colophon. Our work is for the disillusioned and disaffected, the adventurous and independent spirits who thirst for more, who push boundaries and like to witness others test their limits. We know we're not alone. Let's make some noise.

They do not currently accept poetry submissions, and they manage all submissions through Submittable:

www.twodollarradio.submittable.com/submit

Unbridled Books

Greg Michalson
8201 East Highway WW
Columbia, MO 65201
michalsong@unbridledbooks.com
www.unbridledbooks.com

Mystery, Literary Fiction, Novel

For works of fiction, query first by e-mail. Due to the heavy volume of submissions, they regret that they aren't able to consider uninvited manuscripts. However, that is subject to change. Query either Fred Ramey or Greg Michalson, but not both. Their books often reflect a Southern influence, and they've published detective stories and literary fiction.

What to submit:

- A description of your work
- A brief description of your publishing history and a short biography
- 30-50 pages of the manuscript

Fred Ramey and Greg Michalson formed Unbridled Books in 2003, a renewal of their partnership dedicated to publishing high-quality works that are moving, beautiful, and surprising. They chose the name to designate a publishing venture that is both energetic and independent.

Unbridled Books is a premier publisher of works of rich literary quality that appeal to a broad audience. They want to be able to continue their longtime discussion about what allows a novel to touch their hearts and their minds at once. And they want their readers, booksellers, and reviewers to trust that when they pick up an Unbridled book, they're inviting them to enjoy that rarest of pleasures, a good read.

Underground Voices
www.undergroundvoices.com/UVBSubmissions.html

Poetry, Novella, Novel

"In both fiction and nonfiction, there's only one question and one answer. What happened? the reader asks. This is what happened, the writer responds. This... and this... and this, too. Keep it simple. It's the only sure way home."

Underground Voices publishes novels and novellas. They also publish e-shorts (short stories, poetry chapbooks, experimental works). Writing considered for e-shorts should be a minimum of roughly 7,000 words and chapbooks should be a minimum of roughly 50 pages of poetry).

Send submissions to uveditor@undergroundvoices.com, Attn: Jim Tucker, Assistant Editor. Send submissions as a Microsoft Word DOC or as a PDF attachment.

Underground Voices started as an online literary magazine in 2004 publishing hard-hitting, raw, dark fiction, flash fiction and poetry. In 2006, it started publishing an annual print edition, alongside the monthly online issues. In 2009, Underground Voices expanded into a small press. And finally, in 2013, Underground Voices decided to become an independent book publisher only, and aims to publish 1 to 5 books a year.

University of Akron Press
www.uakron.edu/uapress/akron-poetry-prize

Literary Contest, Nonfiction, Poetry

The University of Akron Press awards an annual prize for a book of poetry. Manuscripts must be a total length of at least 48 pages and no longer than 90 pages. Individual poems may have appeared in chapbooks or literary magazines, but they are unable to consider collections that have been previously published as a full-length volume. Translations are not eligible.

Submissions require a $25 fee and are handled through Submittable: www.theuniversityofakronpress.submittable.com/submit

The press also is interested in books on the history and culture of Northeast Ohio. They do not publish fiction.

University of California Press

[Editor's Name]
2120 Berkeley Way
Berkeley, CA 94704
www.ucpress.edu/resources.php?p=authors

Nonfiction, Memoirs, Creative Nonfiction

The University of California Press is one of the largest, most distinguished, and most adventurous scholarly publishers in the world, respected for its creativity and renowned for attracting authors whose work transcends traditional academic boundaries to speak to people everywhere. For more than a century, UC Press has considered manuscripts from the world's foremost scholars, writers, artists, and public intellectuals.

UC Press publishes annually about 200 new books and 40 multi-issue journals in the humanities, social sciences, and natural sciences. About one-fourth of current authors are affiliated with the University of California.

University of California Press publishes general interest and scholarly books in the broad categories listed with the editors' names (www.ucpress.edu/resources.php?p=editors). Generally, they do not publish new fiction, religious inspiration or revelation, children's books, *festschriften*, conference volumes, unrevised dissertations, or autobiographies. Submit to the appropriate editor.

University of Hell Press

www.universityofhellpress.com

Literary Fiction, Poetry

This is a Portland-based literary organization that has recently branched out into fiction. Unsolicited submissions of full-length, well-crafted, well-edited, and completed manuscripts are temporarily suspended. However, their current catalog is evenly divided between solicited and unsolicited works, according to their Submittable page.

www.universityofhellpress.com/submissions/

Check back on this website periodically, or follow their FB page for updates.

University of Hell Press promotes artists who are creating irreverent and thought-provoking works in quiet corners of their worlds. Specializing in intimate literary arts that communicate the human experience with raw views into the everyday condition, University of Hell Press aligns with like-minded individuals who are making their mark through a unique vision and simple, yet heightened, language.

University of Louisiana at Lafayette Press

Attn: Devon Lord
P.O. Box 48231
Lafayette, LA 70504-2831
press.submissions@louisiana.edu
www.ulpress.org/pages/submissions

Story Collection, Creative Nonfiction, Novel, Literary Fiction

This is a regional press with a focus on Louisiana. The Press welcomes submissions of manuscripts pertaining to all facets of Louisiana's history, culture, art, society, politics, economics, religion, ethnicities, and environment. It also welcomes high quality works of fiction and creative nonfiction, but their list is small and highly selective.

The Press gives priority to work of an exemplary caliber, with thorough documentation and a carefully presented argument, that makes a significant, original contribution. Nonfiction manuscripts should be thoroughly documented, with citations to specific sources for quotations and statements that are not common knowledge, and must be based upon research in primary sources.

All manuscripts should adhere to the *Chicago Manual of Style*, with in-house modifications. Accepted manuscripts must be Microsoft Word documents and must be in final form, including all notes and bibliographic material. They strongly recommend authors have their manuscripts proofread and reviewed for grammar, consistency, accuracy, and proper format by others before submission for publication.

Either mail two copies of the manuscript to the address above or send by e-mail.

University of Minnesota Press

Douglas Armato
111 Third Avenue South
Suite 290
Minneapolis, MN 55401-2520
armat001@umn.edu
www.upress.umn.edu/information/for-prospective-ump-authors/editorial-program

Essays, Nonfiction, Memoirs, Novel

Rather than publish traditional scholarly disciplines, UMP publishes books on subjects that range from memoirs, to books about artists and musicians, to histories, and to works of research by sociologists, anthropologists, political scientists.

They try to keep the list evolving, looking for under-explored areas that don't seem to have a publishing "home" or need a new jolt of energy. A recent area where they did this was in studies of *anime* and *manga* cultures, which led them into a very strong program of translating books by Japanese writers. Now they're busy with an education list that focuses not on school "reform" and testing regimes but on the real, everyday problems facing students and parents; one of the first books there was Stuart Biegel's *The Right to Be Out*, an authoritative guide to the legal issues surrounding coming-out in K-12 public schools. Their fiction list is highly selective. To see what they've published, look under the topic of "literature." Their focus is on Minnesota and the Upper Midwest.

University of Nebraska Press

Kristen Elias Rowley
111 Lincoln Mall
Lincoln, NE 68508
krowley2@unl.edu
www.nebraskapress.unl.edu/pages/Authors_Proposal.aspx

Essays, Memoirs, Nonfiction, Creative Nonfiction

The University of Nebraska Press extends the University's mission of teaching, research, and service by promoting, publishing, and disseminating works of intellectual and cultural significance and enduring value.

Founded in 1941, the University of Nebraska Press is a nonprofit scholarly and general interest press that publishes 150 new and reprint titles annually under the Nebraska, Bison Books, and Potomac Books imprints, and in partnership with the Jewish Publication Society, along with 30 journals. As the largest and most diversified university press between Chicago and California, with 4,000 books in print, the University of Nebraska Press is best known for publishing works in Native studies, history, sports, anthropology and geography, American studies and cultural criticism, and creative works.

They are seeking submissions of the highest quality in the following areas for their imprints: American Studies; Anthropology; Creative Works; Early Modern Studies; Environmental Studies; Food and Wine; Geography; History; Literary Criticism; Media Studies; Native-American and Indigenous Studies; Nebraska; Spaceflight; Sports; Women's, Gender, and Sexuality Studies; the American West; Bible and Jewish History; World and National Affairs; Politics; and U.S. and Military History. For specific guidance about what to send, see the website above.

University of New Mexico

1717 Roma Avenue NE
Albuquerque, NM 87106
www.unmpress.com/prospective-authors

Nonfiction

The press does not publish unsolicited fiction, poetry, or children's books. If you are interested in submitting a manuscript to the Press for consideration for publication, please first send an initial query letter and a book proposal to the appropriate acquiring editor, listed on their website. Choose the editor whose subject areas most closely matches the topic of your manuscript. If interested in pursuing your manuscript further, the acquiring editor will request additional materials from you.

Specific topics include field guides, Western film, Southwest adventure, military history, archaeology, literary criticism, memoir, creative nonfiction, and writing guides.

University of North Carolina Press

www.uncpress.org/for-prospective-authors/

Nonfiction

UNCP has a very small fiction list with an emphasis on Thomas Wolfe and anthologies of North Carolina writers.

Check their topics of interest before submitting. These range from Civil War America to Islamic civilization.

University Press of Colorado
www.coloradoreview.colostate.edu/colorado-prize-for-poetry/

Literary Contest, Poetry

The Colorado Prize for Poetry is an international poetry book manuscript contest established in 1995. Each year's prizewinner receives a $2,000 honorarium and publication of his or her book by the Center for Literary Publishing.

There is a $28 fee to submit a manuscript. For more details, go here:

www.coloradoreview.colostate.edu/colorado-prize-for-poetry/submission-guidelines-online/

Unnamed Press

www.unnamedpress.com

Literary Fiction, Story Collection, Novella, Novel, Essays

Unnamed Press is a literary, trendy press with a young MFAish slant. They do get people into bookstores for readings and are big on Tumblr and social media.

The Unnamed Press publishes literature from around the world. Whether it's fiction, memoir or something in between, they are always interested in unlikely protagonists, undiscovered territories and courageous voices. They are distributed by Publishers Group West. Their sister nonprofit press is Phoneme Media.

Queries and submissions can be addressed to the editors at info@unnamedpress.com.

UNO Press

University of New Orleans
138 Liberal Arts Building
New Orleans, LA 70148
(504) 280-7457
unopress@uno.edu
www.unopress.org/lab.aspx

Story Collection, Novel

UNO Press sponsors an annual fiction contest for either a story collection or novel. Submit your manuscript via Submittable.
  www.unopress.submittable.com/submit
  The work does not have to be regionally focused. UNO Press is based at the University of New Orleans and distributed by Hopkins Fulfillment Services. There is no word limit. There is no limit on subjects covered. Works of fiction (novels and short story collections) only. The contest is open to all authors, regardless of publishing history. The submission fee is $28.00, and the winner will receive $10,000 and publication.
  The university collects submissions from March 15 to August 31, deciding on 15-20 finalists. The finalists are read by students in The Publishing Laboratory, a university program. The class will focus on making the book a critical and commercial success upon its release.

Unthank Books

Tania Hershman
P.O. Box 3506
Norwich, Norfolk
United Kingdom NR7 7QP
44 (0) 1603 471300
ashley.stokes@unthankbooks.com
www.unthankbooks.com

Literary Fiction, Essays, Novella, Novel, Fiction, British

Unthank are publishers of adult literary fiction, genre fiction with a distinctive slant, story collections, anthologies, and nonfiction. They very much support first-timers and authors of any profile, age, gender, religious, sexual or political orientation as long as their ambition matches ours.

Submissions should be 80,000 words maximum.

They don't publish poetry, children's fiction, YA, erotica, scripts, and previously self-published work. They can only support U.K.-based writers.

To submit, in the first instance, e-mail Ashley Stokes (at the e-mail address above) the first 50 pages and a synopsis and cover letter.

Sign up for their e-mail list to be notified of their next open reading period.

Urban Farmhouse Press

D.A. Lockhart
Submissions -[Genre name]
P.O. Box 33011
Lakeview R.O.
Windsor, ON
Canada N8Y 1H0
www.urbanfarmhousepress.com/submissions.html

Poetry, Novel, Novella, Fiction

They are now accepting either online or postal submissions. Please send hard copy submissions to the address above with the required fee if applicable. See Submittable for details.

www.urbanfarmpress.submittable.com/submit

Whichever portal you use, be sure to include a short bio and contact information with your submission. All payments are to be made out to Urban Farmhouse Press.

They are looking for book-length manuscripts meeting the following general guidelines:

- Crossroads Poetry Series: minimum 50-60 pages of poetry, single spaced, and one poem per page
- Fiction: minimum 150 pages of prose, 12 pt font, double-spaced
- Novellas: 60-145 pages of prose, 12 pt font, double-spaced
- Cities of the Straits Chapbook Series: 20-40 pages of poetry or fiction, 12 pt font, double-spaced

Submissions open from April to August annually. All manuscripts chosen for publication will receive a book contract and 8% royalties on all print copies sold.

Vagrant Press

Vagrant Press
3660 Strawberry Hill
Halifax, Nova Scotia
Canada B3K 5A9
www.nimbus.ca/about/submissions

Story Collection, Novel, Literary Fiction, Canadian

Vagrant Press, Nimbus Publishing's fiction imprint, is accepting proposals for full-length works of fiction. They regularly accept unsolicited submissions.

Vagrant aims to publish high-quality, original books. They're looking for stories with broad appeal and writing that is modern and innovative. They are dedicated to supporting Atlantic Canadian writers. First consideration will be given to manuscripts written by Atlantic Canadians. (They are only accepting submissions from Canadian citizens at this time.)

www.nimbuspublishing.submittable.com

While they are primarily interested in literary novels, they will consider collections of short fiction. In general, they are not interested in genre fiction (romance, speculative fiction), although they will consider mystery/crime novels.

Include a cover letter with publication credits and contact information, a synopsis, and a writing sample of up to 50 pages.

Veliz Books

info@veliz.com
www.squareup.com/store/veliz-books

Poetry, Novel, Translation, Hispanic

Veliz Books is an independent literary press dedicated to discovering, publishing, and promoting work from emerging and established authors. They seek quality and original literature written in English or Spanish. Veliz Books is also committed to publishing translations into English from Spanish or Portuguese.

Their reading period is from March 2nd through May 2nd of each year. To submit a manuscript, only use their electronic submissions manager.

www.velizbooks.submittable.com/submit

Verse Chorus Press | Dark Passage Books
versechorus@gmail.com
www.versechorus.com

Fiction, Crime, Novel

Verse Chorus Press is an independent publishing house founded in 1998 by Katherine Spielmann and Steve Connell. The press grew out of the music and arts magazine *Puncture*, which they edited from 1982 to 2000. VCP publishes primarily books on music and pop culture, along with music-themed fiction.

Since the birth of its Dark Passage imprint in 2012, VCP has also developed a strong line of crime fiction. Study their list to ensure that your book is a good fit. Then send a query via the e-mail above or use their contact page form.

Vine Leaves Press

vineleavespress@gmail.com
www.vineleavespress.com/submissions.html

Novel, Essays, Australian, Literary Fiction, Story Collection, Poetry,

Want to be published by Vine Leaves Press? If you have a manuscript that you would like them to publish, answer the following questions (in your head):

- Do you believe this manuscript is in the best possible shape?
- Is it edited and proofread to the best of your ability (or someone else's ability)?
- Will your query letter make them need to read your book?
- Does your work suit Vine Leaves Press?

There are three ways to submit. For details see their submissions' page above. They require that authors have a social media presence and be active in the online world. If they accept your book, you will receive a 40% net royalty on all e-book and print sales. They are looking for novels (all genres accepted, but with a literary bent), memoirs, biographies, autobiographies, creative nonfiction, and writing and publishing reference books, and story collections.

To get started, e-mail a query letter, the first ten pages (attached as an Word DOC), and a biography to vineleavespress@gmail.com. Write "Query: Your Book Title" in the subject line. They do not accept snail mail. You will get an automatic response. If you didn't get one, check your spam. If it's not in spam, send it to them again.

They will respond within two months. If they haven't replied to you within two months, follow up.

Waldorf Publishing

2140 Hall Johnson Road
Grapevine, TX 76051
(972) 674-3131
info@WaldorfPublishing.com
www.WaldorfPublishing.com

Novel, Poetry, Fiction, Children, New Writers, Nonfiction

Waldorf Publishing launched in 2013 in the great state of Texas. Waldorf Publishing is female owned, minority owned and small business certified. Waldorf Publishing's goal is not only to produce unique, quality reading for a wide audience, but also to help their authors gain the recognition they deserve.

They have booked their authors into hundreds of media appearances including: CNN, FOX News, BBC, Dr. Drew Pinsky, FOX Business, CBS News, ABC New York, MSNBC, Al Sharpton/Politics Nation, MSNBC-Morning with Joe, The Lip TV, iHeart Radio, NPR, Al Jazeera TV, CBS affiliates, NBC affiliates, FOX affiliates, ABC affiliates, WGN, SIRIUS Radio, FOX Good Day NY, WPIX, *The Guardian Newspaper*, PBS, French Television, Irish National Television, and Radio, *The Globe*, and many more.

There is no info on their website about their submissions' procedures, but they do invite contact via the form on their webpage.

Washington Writers' Publishing House
www.washingtonwriters.org/wwph-annual-contests

Novel, Poetry, Story Collection, Literary Contest, New Writers

The WWPH publishes authors living in the Washington D.C./Baltimore area. Winners of their annual contest receive a publication contract, a $1000 prize, and 50 copies of the book.

Between July 1 and November 15, Washington Writers' Publishing House (WWPH) will accept manuscripts for entry in their annual book competitions, The Jean Feldman Poetry Prize and The Washington Writers' Publishing House Fiction Prize. Writers who live within a 75-mile radius of the U.S. Capitol in the District of Columbia, Maryland and Virginia are eligible to enter these competitions. The winning manuscripts will be published in the fall.

Staffed by previous winners who volunteer their time and skills, WWPH is a non-profit cooperative press reflecting the cultural and racial diversity of the greater Washington, Baltimore and Northern Virginia areas. Judging is traditionally performed by WWPH members who read the anonymous manuscripts. The Submittable page is here:

www.wwph.submittable.com/submit

The winners become members of WWPH and should be prepared to participate actively in the work of the press, including such areas as publicity, distribution, production, and fundraising. Their 37-year tradition of writers working on behalf of other writers is essential to the continued vitality and success of WWPH. Contest entrants should be willing to make this commitment should their work be selected for publication.

Wayne State University Press

The Leonard N. Simons Building
4809 Woodward Avenue
Detroit, MI 48201-1309
www.wsupress.wayne.edu/authors

Nonfiction

Before submitting a proposal to them, consider whether your project is suitable to their list. Currently, they are actively acquiring books in African-American studies, media studies, fairy-tale studies, Jewish studies, citizenship studies, and regional studies. They're also interested in books about the state of Michigan, the city of Detroit, and the Great Lakes region.

Wayne State University Press does not publish unrevised dissertations, *festschriften*, or novels.

Wild Rose Press

www.catalog.thewildrosepress.com
www.thewildrosepress.com/traditionalpublishing

Novel, Romance, Women's Fiction, Historical, Mystery, Thriller, Fantasy, Erotica

The Wild Rose Press, Inc. is a royalty paying publisher. They accept queries from genres other than romance. These include women's fiction, mystery or thriller, historical fiction and erotica. Their titles span the sub-genre spectrum from sweet to sensually erotic in all lengths.

For print books, they are looking for manuscripts 45,000 to 100,000 words. The Wild Rose Press, Inc. contract terms are for 5 years and renew yearly. They employ a full staff of editors and copyeditors. Authors should expect revisions to their contracted work. They have a marketing department, but authors are encouraged to actively promote their work.

They do not accept outside artwork for cover art. Authors have input on the design of the cover, but the final artwork decision remains with The Wild Rose Press, Inc.

Send a query letter containing the following: name, e-mail, and mailing address. Include the word count, a highly detailed synopsis, and the first 5 pages of your manuscript in the body of the e-mail. Do not send attachments: queryus@thewildrosepress.com.

Wildside Press

9 710 Traville Gateway Dr.
Suite 234
Rockville, MD 20850
www.wildsidepress.com

Custom Books, Mystery

This is a publisher for authors whose books have gone out of print. 99.9% of their titles are reprints of previously published books and stories, and most of those are reprinted by Print on Demand (POD). POD prints one copy of a book every time one is sold. POD is not the way to sell millions of books. If that is your goal, your time is better spent with larger New York publishers. Wildside Press is great at republishing books for which there is a steady, small demand—at least 20 copies per year to 1,000 copies per year.

Submissions are currently closed, unless you are an author who was previously published through Wildside Press or have a significant number of older backlist titles or an ongoing series with steady demand that has been dropped by the larger New York publishers. If this is you, contact them, and they'll discuss your project(s).

www.wildsidepress.com/contact/

Willow Books
www.willowlit.net

Literary Contest, Literary Fiction, Novel, Poetry

For writers of color and underrepresented populations, this is a publisher to check out. Willow Books Literature Awards result in book publications, readings, and a cash prize. One prize is for poetry and the other for fiction. It's $25 to enter either the Open Readings Period or the Literature Awards. Use their Submittable link for specifics.

www.aquariuspress.submittable.com/submit

The mission of Willow Books is to develop, publish and promote writers typically underrepresented in the literary field. An independent press with a woman of color at its helm, Aquarius Press/Willow Books is recognized as an industry leader for its commitment to artistic development.

In addition to publishing, Willow provides a national platform for its authors to engage with the public through readings, workshops, conferences, competitions, and streaming broadcasts across the country. Several of Willow's authors have earned fellowships, post-graduate degrees and faculty tenure due in large part to being published by the press. Key partnerships have been formed with many institutions of higher learning and organizations such as PEN/Faulkner, Busboys & Poets/Teaching for Change, and Cave Canem. Your continued support of their authors enables them to honor their mission.

Wings Press

www.books-by-wings-epress.com/general-fiction-submission

Romance, YA Fiction, Novel

Wings ePress, Inc. is dedicated to producing and marketing the best in fiction of all genres except erotica. When you send your work to them, they will review it with the highest of professional standards and quickly contact you with their assessment of your submission.

Know that Wings does not accept manuscripts containing scenes of rape. Do not send them simultaneous submissions, and make sure your manuscript does not have any pictures in the content. Word count should be from 40,000 to 120,000 words.

On the cover page, in the upper left hand corner, give them your name, address, city, state and zip, phone number and e-mail address. Center the name of your book, your author name, the genre and an approximate word count. Do not double space the text or use a double space between sentences.

Currently, Wings is seeking manuscripts in the following catagories:

- All general fiction
- Young Adult: paranormal, fantasy and animal stories (dog, horses, cats and odd pets can be in the animal's POV)

For more, go to their website. Submit all manuscripts to submissions@books-by-wings-epress.com.

Winter Goose Publishing
www.wintergoosepublishing.com/submissions

Women's Fiction, Novella, Story Collection, Poetry, Romance, Novel, Mystery, YA Fiction, Fantasy, Thriller, Creative Nonfiction

Sign up for their newsletter, and they will tell you when they're open again. The kinds of books they've published in the past include the following:

- Fiction
- Action/Adventure
- Suspense
- Fantasy
- Mystery
- Romance (Primarily Contemporary, Romantic Suspense and Paranormal, but will consider others)
- Young Adult
- General
- Creative nonfiction
- Poetry and Prose Poetry (focusing on contemporary poets, but rarely publishing anthologies or single pieces by non WGP authors)

Winterwolf Press

questions@winterwolfpress.com
www.winterwolfpress.com

Novel, Fiction, Fantasy, Science Fiction

Winterwolf Press loves books that inspire as well as entertain. They are dedicated to publishing fiction and nonfiction that promote peace, joy, magic and positivity. They especially gravitate toward fantasy, science fiction, and paranormal fiction stories with these qualities. For nonfiction, they look for works that will help their readers grow in their personal and spiritual development. Please do not send dystopian novels.

For fiction, submit only completed and edited manuscripts. They love nonfiction that has a different angle and impact. Their main focus leans toward alternative medicine, personal development, spirituality, and self-help.

Here are the guidelines for manuscript submission:

- One page query letter
- One page synopsis of the novel with spoilers
- The first three chapters
- Word DOC, TXT, or PDF formats only
- No manuscripts over 120,000 words

They do accept global submissions and will get back to you if they are interested in your work. For specific questions, contact them at questions@winterwolfpress.com.

Wising Up Press

Heather Tosteson
P.O. Box 2122
Decatur, GA 30031-2122
(404) 276-6046
comments@universaltable.org
www.universaltable.org/wisingup.html

Anthology, International, Poetry, Story Collection, Novel, Nonfiction, Essays

Wising Up Press has specific interests. They are looking for the following:

- Works exploring the impact of illness, written from the points of view of those experiencing illness, accompanying those who are ill, or those who treat illness;
- Works exploring the challenges and choices and cultural and identity shifts for first-generation citizens who have chosen to enter into mutually transforming conversation with a new, chosen culture. They are particularly interested in work by women who have immigrated to the United States from countries and cultures with marked gender inequality;
- Works exploring the frontline of pluralism, for example, what it means to live up close, unvarnished, and inextricably personal with profound differences of temperament, ability, race, religion, and culture;
- Works exploring the joys, challenges, surprises and sorrows of living into the full richness and complexity of age;
- Works exploring the mystery of psychological and social resilience in the face of serious familial, social, economic, or health challenges, with a special focus on those who experience both early adversity and the beneficial impact of counteracting social forces.

They often use different e-mail submission addresses, depending on their calls for manuscripts. Please check their website above for current calls.

World Castle Publishing
www.worldcastlepublishing.net

YA Fiction, Novel

All authors are invited to submit their work, including unrepresented authors and unpublished authors. They ask you to review their submission guidelines carefully.

At this time, they are only accepting electronically submitted manuscripts. This allows a timely review of submissions.

This is your opportunity to sell yourself and your writing to them. Make it count. Make sure the manuscript has been painstakingly edited and polished. Also send them a short synopsis of the book.

- Expect a six to eight-week turnaround on your submission. If you have not heard back from them by then, feel free to e-mail them requesting a status update.
- No simultaneous submissions. Submit your work to only one publisher at a time.

For detailed information, see their guidelines.
www.worldcastlepublishing.net/submission-guidelines

When submissions reopen, send the manuscript to this address: submissions.worldcastle@gmail.com. They will accept previously published works, but only if the author holds exclusive rights.

Zero Books
www.johnhuntpublishing.com/zer0-books

Essays, British, Novel

John Hunt Publishing/Zero Books is a new kind of publishing company, based on a more equitable author/publisher relationship. For their authors they provide an automated production system, forums, and a marketing database with over 40,000 contacts and other online tools to produce and market each book. They partner with their authors on marketing, reaching all the traditional bookstore markets for print books, worldwide, and all online retailers.

The vast majority of their new titles come from existing authors recommending others to come to them, or from booksellers' recommendations. They focus on the "mid-list" rather than celebrity. mass-market publishing on the one hand or highly academic on the other. They're looking for good popular writing; the new, non-generic, ambitious and risky. They particularly enjoy the books that cross boundaries and push out the envelope, that are in their way unusual or definitive (or both).

To get started, find the right imprint for your book. See their list here:

www.zero-books.net/imprints.html

Once you're figured out which imprint is right for you, go here and select the imprint. Use their submission form.

www.johnhuntpublishing.com/

Say something about who your book is aimed at, how you reckon it's going to sell, what your qualifications for writing it are and attach as much text as you have (upload a Microsoft Word DOC or PDF). It doesn't matter if it's not finished yet, but they can't respond to questions like "I've got an idea about writing a book, how do I go about it and would you publish it." If it looks to them like a good possibility, they'll usually respond within 24 hours.

Zest Books

www.zestbooks.net/opportunities

Novel, YA Fiction

To submit a book proposal, first see their other books and make sure that your proposal is in line with their mission, audience, and tone. Then send them:

- a brief description of the book you are proposing;
- a sample table of contents;
- a sample (1-5 pages) of proposed text in their style (conversational, intelligent, and current);
- any competitive research you've done on the topic;
- your resume;
- and 3 to 5 published writing samples/selections.

Because Zest has a unique mission statement, they often develop new book concepts in-house. They then contact their Zest Author Pool, a vetted selection of authors, to see who is interested in developing their book idea into a proposal. If they like the proposal, they hire the author!

If you're interested in becoming a member of their Author Pool, send a cover letter stating why you are interested in young adult nonfiction, plus your specific areas of interest and specialties, your resume, and 3 to 5 writing samples/selections.

Send all information to: dan@zestbooks.net.

Zumaya Publications
www.zumayapublications.com/

Story Collection, Crime, Romance, Thriller, Novel

Zumaya considers almost any genre, but they expect their authors to get out there and hustle for their books. Read their guidelines thoroughly so that you understand this is a Print-On-Demand (POD) Press. They will not be able to get you into bookstores.

www.zumayapublications.com/guidelines/Guidelines.pdf

The publisher doesn't pay advances. Your book begins earning you money the moment it goes on sale. Sales will depend on your willingness to market your book and promote yourself. They help as much as they can, given limited staff and a tight budget. On the other hand, they contract only for the rights they're going to use, leaving you free to sell or use the others as you see fit.

All genres are welcome; however, submitted books should fit with one of their imprints. This isn't to say they wouldn't consider a beautifully written manuscript that doesn't meet those requirements. They just know from experience those are rare. They publish one short story collection a year; the stories need to have a unifying theme of place: geographical, emotional, or psychological.

They look for multi-dimensional, believable characters, good pacing and solid plotting. The minimum word count for adult fiction is 50,000 words and up. The minimum for juvenile fiction is 40,000 and up. They are aware that children's lit writers are being told a smaller word count is preferred. Not here.

They do not accept queries by surface mail. To submit your query, complete the online form:

www.zumayapublications.com/submissions.php.

Acknowledgments

Thank you for reading *The Big Book of Small Presses & Independent Publishers*. I hope you found it inspiring and enlightening. If you did, I would greatly appreciate you leaving a review on the review site of your choice.

Reviews are crucial for any author, and a line or two about your experience can make a huge difference. If you're part of the Goodreads' community, comments there are especially valuable.

www.goodreads.com

This book owes a debt of gratitude to Brian Grove, who, prior to his death, provided a weekly newsletter called My Perfect Pitch. Brian faithfully sent out the names and contact information of independent publishers who were open to authors who couldn't find an agent. Because of Brian Grove, I began entering these names into Outlook, and eventually, using Outlook's ability to create categories, I developed a database of publishers. I tagged the publisher according to the genres of fiction the company was willing to consider. Over the years, I have been able to help many subscribers to my website (www.maryleemacdonaldauthor.com) find publishers for their books.

Eventually, I began to think that the information I had collected might be useful to other writers who were frustrated by the endless agent hunt. I personally know three fine authors with amazing novels. These authors had spent twenty years trying to get their books published in New York. One self-published her book, and the other two gave up. Today, their books exist only in manuscript. That left an ache in my heart.

As anyone who is at all plugged into the online writing world knows, there is a groundswell of literary activity. In spite of how busy we all are, people somehow find time to write. That's because so many of us have stories to tell, stories that matter.

All over the country, even in places not normally regarded as "writing Meccas," small pockets of committed authors are putting their hearts and souls into their work. These writers range from young people who are avid readers of fantasy and speculative fiction—and who turn out in droves for Comicon—to older writers who finally have space and time to write the kinds of books they've always loved: mysteries, short stories, romances, women's fiction, memoirs, or literary fiction.

When I was the Writer-in-Residence for the City of Mesa Public Library, I met many of these writers, and I have had a hand in helping some of them connect with publishers mentioned in this book. These writers made me think that the effort it took to put this book together might be a worthwhile endeavor.

If you have a favorite publisher, one who has helped bring your book into the world, please let me know through the contact page on one of my websites.

Facebook
www.facebook.com/MaryleeMacD

Twitter
www.twitter.com/MaryleeMacD

Websites
www.maryleemacdonaldauthor.com

www.maryleemacdonald.com

www.maryleemacdonald.org

About the Author

Before turning to fiction, Marylee MacDonald worked as a carpenter and magazine editor. Her nonfiction has appeared in *Sunset, Better Homes & Gardens*, the *Journal of Light Construction*, and the *Old-House Journal*. She holds a Master's in English/Creative Writing from San Francisco State, and her short stories have won the Barry Hannah Prize, the Jeanne M. Leiby Memorial Chapbook Award, the *American Literary Review Fiction Prize*, the Ron Rash Award, *New Delta Review's* Matt Clark Prize, and many others.

She is the author of *Montpelier Tomorrow, Bonds of Love & Blood, The Rug Bazaar*, and *Body Language*. When she's not writing, she's walking on a beach, strolling in a redwood forest, plucking snails from her tomatoes, or hiking in the red rocks of Sedona.

Made in United States
North Haven, CT
12 July 2024

54711580R00212